The female has arrived

4 seasons in 4 weeks

Awakening the Power, Wisdom, & Beauty in Every Woman's Nature

Suzanne Mathis McQueen

Tobacco Road Press
Ashland, Oregon

With enormous gratitude to

Editor: Jessica Vineyard, Red Letter Editing
Book Design: Jeff Altemus, Align Visual Arts & Communication
Development Editor: Janis Hunt Johnson, Ask Janis Editorial
Cover Design: Gaelyn Larrick
Working Book Cover and Social Media Graphics: Ian Backer
Chapter Artwork: Mara Friedman
Chart Designs: Andrew Bonsall
Additional Artwork: Mara Friedman, Betty LaDuke, Inger Jorgenson, Cat Stone (Hawkins), Jen Otey, Louise Abel Curtis, Cathy McClelland, Krista Lynn Brown, Clio Wondrausch, Pegi Smith, Lorraine Leslie, Victoria Christian, Denise Kester, Damian Fulton, Cecile Miranda, and Tzila "Z" Duenzl

Special thanks to advisors and support team

Publishing Consultants: Christy Collins and Steve Scholl, White Cloud Press and Confluence Books Services; Developmental Advisors: Cynthia Salbato, Meri Walker, and Taylor Gimbel; Copy Consulting: Sierra Faith; Web Consultant: Ed Taylor; Webmaster: Buzzboosters; Hormone Consulting: Mary Lou Follett, NP, Faith Bonsall, RN, Christine Hitchcock, PhD research assistant, Center for Menstrual Cycle and Ovulation Research (CeMCOR), University of British Columbia, Vancouver, and Dana Nelson, RPh, MS, FASCP; Draft copy printing: Fidelity Quick Print, Central Point, Oregon; Q*Cardz: Patti Halprin

Additional heartfelt appreciation goes to

my former husband, Wade McQueen, who, as an anatomy instructor back in the 1990s, opened my awareness to the deeper hormonal intricacies of my design, and for continuing to have my back over the years; my kids, Ian, Preston, and Myan, for living with a mother who, for years, continued to state, "The book is almost done", yet never seemed to give up on me; daughter-in-law, Kristi, because she's awesome in every way; my sister, Rosemary, for caring for our parents while I continued to state, "The book is almost done," and who also tossed in good ideas from time to time; my mother, who notices the smallest of beautiful touches; my father in spirit, who seems to stay with and protect me, giving me courage when I need it; Richard Shepard, my high school pal who insisted that I share my 4s4w system with the world; the lovely and enlightened sex education instructor, Feather Gilmore, who also convinced me that this understanding was needed; the poet, Matt Hill, for teaching me that reading an old love letter, clever wordsmithing, and a good Indian curry are good for the heart and a smile; Jon Miller, the fire chief and great date who rescued and babysat me through an extremely tough time and never let me down; and to Ms. Sunshine herself (and author/online marketing machine), Pam Hogan, for encouraging me, one phone call at a time, every week, for just about ever.

More personal love and thanks to the following friends and / or professional associates over a seven-year span

Gloria Feldt, Jane Hardwicke Collings, Moriah Hayes, Dr. Debi Yohn, Karen Lovely, Sandra Baker, Mathis/Backer/McQueen/Smith/Force clans, Barbara Whelan, Mary McJilton Benarth, Anita Assaf, Audrey Pope, Claire Peterson, Robyn Parnell, Eric & Susan Wallengren, Don Chasey, Susan Amari Gold, Barbara Peeters, Colleen Pyke, Wendy Connor, Maylee Otto, Cori Magarian, Patty Bonsall, Shelley Lotz, Terry Van Blargen Procknow, Ginny Miller, Rachael Ridley, Amy Shuman, Julie Meade, Linda Jolly, Violet Smith, Tim Paulsen, Tom Antion, Richard Paul Evans, Robert G. Allen, Dian Thomas, Joycebelle Edelbrock, Debbie Thornton, Sheri Croy, Michael Gurian, Debbie Bermont, Teri Lux, Ann Chasey, Kenny Lapham, David Kurrasch, Eric Christiansen, Cam Newman, Bruce Rawles, Elizabeth Gould, Anya de Marie, the Red Web Foundation, Kami Wycoff & She Writes, The Ashland Resource Center, Mike Varner, Georgene Crowe, Gretchen Lee, Lucinda Kay, Joan Heiken, Heather Jenard, Leilani Kahananui, Aunt Yvonne, Monique Bourin, Jeanne Normand White, Dave Shellabarger, Hālau Hula o Nā Pua o Hawaiʻi Nei, Ka Piʻo O Ke Ānuenue, The Phoenix staff, Denise Ross, Wylie & Ginny Carlisle, Kate Wasserman, Napili Gaston, Rebecca Elston, Allison Hamik, Jessica Johnson Zarganes, Estelle Abel, Bookwise/Writewise, Kathleen & Scott, Lisa Schumacher, Winn Frankland, Ashland Book Club 1, RoseMarie & LindaMarie Greenburg, Mary McGuire, Kim Wright, Jaya Opela, Cilette Swan, Alice DiMicele, Rogue Suspects, Sterling Oldham, Jules Pierce, Alice Cuellar, Jerry & Christine Molinero, Belinda Hein, Bobcat, Cecily Thornton, Jeff Pevar, Genie Long, Lisa Rand, Dave & Scott, Angela Gentle, my supportive Facebook friends, University Toastmasters, SAHS Classmates of '75, and last, but certainly not least, the Rogue Valley Firecracker Queens.

Inspirations / Muses

Gloria Steinem, Suzanne Somers, Jean Houston, T.S. Wiley, and Ellen DeGeneres (she dances).

Disclaimer

All material and claims expressed within are based on the author's observation, reason, experience, opinion, and, for lack of a better explanation, divine guidance, as well the author's personal survey studies. No scientific studies have been done to prove this approach valid or invalid. This is an approach developed to assist one's management of her scientifically proven hormonal rhythm. Each human rhythm is unique and subject to tracking and interpreting on an individual basis, since each monthly rhythm is subject to alterations based on the individual's unique circumstances, health, and self-care regimen.

This book in no way makes any medical claims or gives medical advice by the author, only perspective advice. Of course, please do not make any radical changes to your personal care routine without consulting your health care provider. Tracking of one's personal hormonal rhythm is intended to help her understand her health and well-being, assist medical practitioners in helping their patients and clients, and highlights the need for immediate and increased research in women's health and well-being.

For Myan,
whose name means
"Water from the Spring"

And to three radiant stars,

Eleanor Guage Geddes,
the girl from New York who always believed in me,

Kumu Hula Raylene Ha'alelea Kawaiae'a,
who embodied sacred feminine aloha,

Frederick Eli Mathis,
my father, who believed in following the woman's lead and final
say when it came to her reproductive body and future.

Contents

Section III: Women's Work

Conclusion: The Female Has Arrived

Epilogue

Foreword

As a psychotherapist in private practice, I often meet women who are exhausted and deeply confused. I see faces of quiet trauma bearing many of life's countless burdens; I have listened to hundreds of women who are existing in a haze, a deeply traumatized state. It seems to me that the greatest trauma I stand witness to is the unspoken pact by women to dismiss their own feelings, intuition, and non-intellectual intelligence in the hope of belonging and finding acceptance. In their journeys through growth and healing these women come alive when they begin to question the state of affairs, when they turn off the static noise coming from outside and tune in to their *inner station*, their own inner voice.

I have learned to trust my intuition about people. When I met Suzanne she instantly felt like a sister to me. When we share time together I feel a deep connection to myself, my wisdom as a woman, and my place in the world. Her natural passion for her global sisters, their inherent rights, and their buried wisdom, along with her deep personal understanding of her own Authentic Feminine, uniquely qualifies her to deliver this book's powerful message.

The book *4 Seasons in 4 Weeks* is an enthusiastic celebration of women and their contribution to our planet. It is also a warning that the peripheral social position women currently occupy is costly not only for women but for all beings.

Both women and men will find a body of enjoyable and pertinent information within the covers of this book. The wisdom on these pages expounds upon our knowledge of women's physical, emotional, and mental cycles. It is not only an invitation to take responsibility for our own lives, but to understand ourselves more fully. This book is a map on how to do it, a step-by-step exploration of our own mysterious landscape. As I was gobbling page after page I felt held in a beautiful way, supported and guided by a gentle and faithful sister on my journey back home.

—Maria A. Connolly
MS, LPC

Spring passes and one remembers one's innocence.
Summer passes and one remembers one's exuberance.
Autumn passes and one remembers one's reverence.
Winter passes and one remembers one's perseverance.
—Yoko Ono

Prologue
The Mystery & the Message

My Story

All I can tell you is that I had an experience. Other people speak of a "near death" awakening as they were drowning, or in a car crash, during which a powerful message was delivered right at the moment of doom. They swore they'd change their ways if only God would save them at that very moment. Not me. I was simply on a lunch break from work, at home in my kitchen, looking at my day planner where I had been tracking my feminine cycle for the past few months.

It is as vivid now as the day it happened in 1998. The words "fall, winter, spring, and summer" floated to the surface and hovered over my calendar. I heard myself say, "Hmmm, my cycle looks just like the four seasons."

Maybe it doesn't sound like much of a revelation, but in what probably amounted to a nano-second, my physical health, my job as a business owner working with female employees and clients, my history of women's advocacy, and my romantic relationships all aligned perfectly. I was shown four distinguishable weeks that blend together beautifully, each one highly important for setting the stage for the next. From that day forward, I began to predict how I'd feel during the upcoming days throughout my *whole cycle*. I began to understand the pattern of a rhythm I didn't know I had (or tried to ignore). This rhythm eventually became an integral part of my day planner.

Yet, it was more than this—a lot more. As if a secret, a sacred memory, was unlocked and released from my deeply buried ancestral treasure chest, this very big picture and understanding was presented, or gifted, to me. Call it Divine Guidance from my greatest grand-mothers or my super-logical brain just "seeing" how it all fits together; I was shown a blueprint for something rich and powerful that goes well beyond our health. A woman's organic rhythm influences communal attitudes and global politics. It shows why gender-balanced decisions are so crucial to our planet's survival. It reveals why all attempts to take sovereignty away from women will never succeed, nor should. To speak of the feminine cycle on its own would be to speak of it out of context. It is completely in context, interconnected with the vast web of natural universal rhythms and human behaviors, past, present, and future.

When I was convinced by my high school friend, Richard, and my guru-girlfriend-and-health-expert, Feather, to share my super-simple "system" with others, I thought it would only take me two months to write it down. It took seven years. Every time I thought I was near the end, I'd wake up at 3 or 4:00 AM with a new, huge "download" of information to include in the book. Broader insights kept coming, and I took it as a sign to keep going. This was something I was supposed to teach. I was "being called," as they say. I believe that we all are.

Women and men kept asking me for the information. Through my research I discovered that, though the feminine cycle has been extensively written about (and continues to be), *even including a comparison to the four seasons*, there is still a need to understand it more deeply—to actually make a connection to it, as well as to remove the embarrassment of it. The best I can do is to share what I saw, what was gifted to me, what I implemented, how I integrated what I knew to be true before that, and how this simple way of looking at my cycle changed my life—how it completes the way I view the world. My own lifetime study of people, observation, logic, and gleanings from teachers, mentors, inspirational individuals, and interesting stories dovetail and align beautifully with this new understanding. It's sensual, spiritual, political, philosophical, connected, and deeply personal.

I give thanks and respect to all of the people who are currently talking or writing about the same subjects as I present, with their own interpretations of them. I encourage you to check them out. My goal is to have women feel the best that they can, encourage our relationships to be the best they can be, and create a culture of peace on our planet as quickly as possible. Find the translation that resonates with you. There are often many messengers and many ways to look at a subject when the time is right to bring it to our attention. I greatly appreciate your interest in my version of this amazing topic.

—Suzanne
Summer, 2012
Ashland, Oregon

There are Several Ways to Read this Book

1. To get the greatest value from this book, read it from beginning to end. The chapters build upon each other.

2. Just open it anywhere and start reading. Each piece of information is part of a whole, yet also stands on its own just fine.

3. Go directly to the 4 Seasons in 4 Weeks section by flipping to the color-coded pages. Read each chapter in its entirety.

4. Go directly to the 4 Seasons in 4 Weeks section. Read only the bullet points for a quick glimpse.

5. Reverse the order of these instructions. Start small and build up to reading the whole book.

6. Read the "To-Do List" at the end of each chapter and get moving!

7. Honor Yourself. You are a uniquely beautiful Being, and important.

Definitions, Interpretations, & Explanations

TERMS

4 Seasons in 4 Weeks: The idea that each week of the four-week feminine cycle represents one season in the year

4s4w: 4 Seasons in 4 Weeks

Feminine Cycle: Female Cycle

Female Recycling System: The Rhythmic Feminine Cycle

Ovulation: The process of an egg being released from the ovary into the fallopian tube for the opportunity to connect with a sperm

Emoping: Emotional Period; the natural process of eliminating emotions through tears, pores, and voice during the fourth week of the cycle, replacing the "syndrome" idea of PMS (pre-menstrual syndrome)

Mind Moods: The different viewpoints that women cycle through at each phase of their rhythm

The Venus Week®[1]: The term coined by Rebecca Booth, M.D., describing the week in the cycle when estrogen rises to its peak

Rhythmic Eating: Eating according to what is best for the cycle today, as well as for the upcoming days; preparing for the upcoming week to prevent unwanted cycle symptoms

Libido: Sex drive

The Authentic Female: The true self when fear, dishonesty, unhealthy behaviors, and society's expectations and historical oppressions are removed

Archetypes of the Authentic Female: The cast of archetypes who emerge with each phase of the female recycling system: Queen, Visionary, Artist, Builder, Fun Date, Lover, Goddess, Wise Woman, World Leader, Athlete, Fire Walker, and Monk; each one shines brighter as you dust her off and begin to see her gifts

Womb Wisdom: The rhythmically intelligent blueprint of the female; well-rounded

Pre-Bloods: Girls who have not yet started their menses, from birth to puberty

Blood-Givers: Females who bleed monthly

Blood-Keepers: Women who no longer bleed for any reason (hysterectomy, menopause, etc.)

Ovulation Nation: The female gender; the tribe that consists of all females on the planet, bound in unity by virtue of the natural rhythm within them; originally designed to support ovulation

Sacred Feminine and Sacred Masculine: The most elevated, balanced, and mature version of the gender selves that live within each person; the essence of the big picture, right brained, Sacred Feminine with holding and transforming energy; and the essence of the laser-focused, left-brained Sacred Masculine with protective energy

Sacred Union: Ultimate right and left brain balance within each individual

Sacred Feminist: One who claims her full Authentic Female Nature, instinct, power, and expression as not only her divine and equal right, but as her responsibility to universal service

Source: The origin of creation; any individual interpretation or belief of it including, but not limited to, science, God, or Goddess, and their respective names, culturally or religiously. The 4s4w approach does not promote, criticize, or judge this individual interpretation or belief; while acknowledging universal and female rhythms as a fact of life, who or what they were created by makes no difference for the purpose of recognizing, interpreting, and teaching the symbolic wisdom found within these natural rhythms, according to the 4s4w system

Women's Work: Depending on the culture, there have always been certain jobs that have been considered "women's work," such as washing the dishes or scrubbing the toilets; the 4s4w system rejects all but one as exclusive to women: tracking and caring for their reproductive bodies, the only true "women's work"

HORMONES

Estrogen: The generic term for any hormone that has estradiol actions on the body tissues; I use this term for simplicity's sake throughout the book

Estradiol: The most important and powerful estrogen, responsible for the development of the female body characteristics and the growth of the uterus, fallopian tubes, breasts, vagina, and outside genitalia; it stimulates the growth of the uterine wall during the first half of the cycle

Progesterone: Pre-Gestation; this hormone prepares, supports, and maintains the uterine "nest"—the pregnancy environment

Testosterone: The hormone of desire; encourages the sex drive and produces progesterone

Blastocyst: Fertilized egg

Follicle Stimulating Hormone: Stimulates egg production from follicles in the ovaries

Luteinizing Hormone: Triggers Ovulation

Things to Know About 4s4w

This book, *4 Seasons in 4 Weeks* (4s4w), is my guide to the natural monthly hormonal rhythm of women, also known as the female cycle, which from here on out I will refer to as the "feminine cycle." *Practically* and *realistically*, it is a monthly sex cycle, energy cycle, and *mental rejuvenation* cycle. It is the most profound piece of our being.

Technically, it's a *reproduction* cycle we're talking about here, with all kinds of names and terms that no one finds comfortable or remembers very well. In this book I use *technical* terms only *when needed*. The truth is, we humans live a *non-technical* existence when it comes to our bodies—we *experience*, we *feel*, and we do a lot of guessing. We do our best to make sense of our relationships, opportunities, circumstances, and gifts. The feminine cycle helps us to be attentive to raising the bar on all of these things. It is a 'round the clock, ongoing life *experience* and causes us to *feel* one way, and then another. Because of this fact, I use analogies and symbolism. I personally learn better and remember more when meaning and application are attached to my *experiences* and *feelings*, rather than from knowledge deposited into my memory bank. The biology doesn't mean much until we can apply it to something we can relate to in our everyday lives.

Reproduction really translates to *sex* and *creation*. Both can be sacred, and both can be exploited. Both are controversial, and so are women because of them. Politics and beliefs surrounding these "women's issues" are passionately contested. I spend a lot of time in this book connecting the dots. With what I find to be a twist of intrigue, the empowering or diminishing treatment of the womb plays an enormous role in our most potent personal and communal issues: healthcare, poverty, spirituality, relationships, the environment, morals, and power politics. I go there.

To keep my writing more focused (and to keep my editor from wringing my neck), this book is written primarily for and *to* adult cycling women, but it contains important understandings for non-cycling women as well. A big part of this message is that our bodies contain a rhythm from the time we are born *until the time we die*—it is present *before* menses begins and continues *after* menopause. The cycle simply *reveals* the rhythm and meaning to us during our reproductive years, embodying and presenting our sacred wisdom on a silver platter for us to identify. The pattern of this rhythm may *adjust* itself throughout life, but be assured: it is always present in our female totality. Our bodies, minds, and spirits are wired together to support this rhythm.

Men who want a connected relationship also benefit greatly from this information. The 4s4w system is one that guys "get" very easily, and can offer guidance on how and when to initiate sex and other connective communication. This book goes deeply into the symbolism of women's lives as leaders and lovers, as we regain sovereignty over our bodies and futures, while still craving and desiring a connection with our men, our heroes, more than ever. It is time we teach men about the sacredness of the female in order for them to begin, both personally and globally, to support and protect rather than dominate and control. I have created short sections toward the end of each "weekly" chapter specifically for the guys. I address couples throughout, because I believe most of us either have a partner or we want one.

I also need to be clear that when I write "he" it could also mean "she," as in "partner." This book is for everyone and anyone who is interested in creating an honored relationship. This book is for all who seek a balanced world where *everyone* is included in the ongoing effort to manifest peace and harmony, health and abundance for all.

We want our men to get in sync with us, but ultimately it is we who need to get this down for our own personal health and well-being. It is in our best interest as women to be in charge of and use our hormones to fuel our powerful female cores rather than let them be in charge of *us*. This area is the only *real* "women's work," and no one else *can* or *may* be in charge of it. It is our responsibility alone. Give this away and you give your *self* away. We can't expect anyone else to understand us if we don't truly understand ourselves.

Throughout the book, I refer to God and all various names and interpretations of the original creation of the Universe, including Science, as *Source* (with an exception here or there). This term is universal and not faith-specific. As women, whether we follow different belief systems or none at all, our cycle binds us in unity.

It is impossible for me to talk about the womb in any sort of responsible way without including some historical background. Talking briefly about women's history has proven to be tricky. I'm a white woman who lives in the United States. This lineage is not the lineage of every woman, but it is the one through which I share this wisdom. I use this story because it briefly tells the progression of the *legality* of female voting and reproduction rights in the U.S., no matter what our color or nationality. My education and research tells me that women's history in other countries is sometimes similar, yet often much more horrific. Please know that I honor and acknowledge you and your history while telling the story that is most familiar to me.

I quote notables and I quote friends. I am not interested in the credentials of the person, only the wisdom of their thoughts. Grammatically, I capitalize many words that are not normally capitalized. Words such as "Nature" and "Period" are significant characters in our feminine cycles and I want them to stand out, so I treat them as proper nouns rather than in their common usage. I capitalize other words for emphasis here and there.

I refer to sex throughout, so it will be up to you to decide what is appropriate for your teen to read. I continue to work on a series of age-appropriate and culturally relevant books to complete this project. Because I am talking about being "in tune" with your natural hormonal rhythm, I want to be very clear that I am in *favor* of birth control. I am not promoting "going without" if you are having sex—at all—or even the Rhythm Method of birth control (unless you're a true expert at it).

Ultimately, while the feminine cycle may be about reproduction, there are a multitude of messages that weave through and support it to give us a naturally rhythmic blueprint for living holistically even beyond our cycling years. May you uncover yours with joy.

The Female Recycling System

Our energetic reproductive bodies are made up of mental-rejuvenation, physical, and sexual systems that work in unison for one month, and then continually repeat the pattern until pregnancy or menopause occurs. The Female *Recycling* System is actually about building and purging, gaining and letting go. We build a home in two weeks in preparation for a possible pregnancy, live in it for a few days, and then take it down when conception does not occur.

My system, 4 Seasons in 4 Weeks, is a way *to think about* how these energy systems work by simply recognizing patterns that are the same each month and to remember the best ways to prepare for and respond to them for the best experience. You can choose to remember just the basics, or study it in depth for an optimal understanding of yourself.

My hope is that the more you recognize these rhythms, the more you'll think about your daily and weekly hormonal changes as a predictable rhythm that you can manage and utilize to live a happier, healthier, more *productive* life.

The Premise

The premise of 4s4w is simple: I break down the approximately 28 days of the monthly cycle into four guided weeks, revealing the logical, easy-to-understand hormonal sequence of women. I call these four weeks of a month *the four weekly seasons* or *the Moon seasons*: Fall, Winter, Spring, and Summer, because the general effect that the constantly changing hormones have on a woman's body have similarities with the characteristics of these seasons. This is the basic concept for an easy-to-remember system. As you get to know your own cycle, you will begin to understand where to break it down even further. I now break mine down daily.

The Purpose

The 4s4w strategy takes this seemingly overwhelming body function and walks you through each week in a non-technical way in order to prepare, manage, and have control over your experience, rather than living a life of *reacting* to it.

Once you understand how, in four weeks, your body goes through your own four seasons just as we have in Nature, you'll understand how each week prepares for the next. You'll begin to see the power you have to take charge of your health, conquering pre-Period symptoms and other discomforts, while taking advantage of its benefits.

The Sacred Feminist

1. Societal Rhythms

The Female Rhythm &
Living in Sync with Others

History, despite its wrenching pain,
cannot be unlived, but if faced with
courage, need not be lived again.
—Maya Angelou

Challenges & Purpose

When it comes to "Periods," Mother Nature doesn't care whether you're black, white, purple, or polka-dotted, Republican or Democrat, Buddhist or atheist, straight or gay, as long as you're a human female and somewhere between the ages of 7 and 55ish. Minus pregnancies, nursing, hysterectomies, or some unusual health challenge, women cycle day in and day out for about 40 years of their lives. Yet this basic function of what makes us female is an uncomfortable, if not taboo, subject. Due to lack of information, embarrassment, or violence against them, women worldwide often suffer in silence from its sometimes chaotic effects, which influence their lives in every way, including parenting, friendships, and sexual relationships.

Women Don't Feel Well

Through my contact with employees, clients, co-workers, students, friends, and family, I have noticed a consistent up-and-down monthly pattern to the way women physically feel, and therefore struggle to keep it all together, often without the psychological support of anyone else. The majority of women I talk to say their monthly cycles disrupt their lives in some way, yet they don't know how to tame the lion. They just don't feel well on a regular basis. I see most women going 24/7 no matter what is happening with them personally. Often they are quietly dealing with heavy bleeding, ongoing fatigue, extreme breast tenderness, or headaches while working and taking care of the family. It would help a lot if their guys could understand.

The Guys

As a gender, men are taught to accept that women are not understandable. However, most men I know or talk to *would* like to understand. They swim in a woman's ocean—they see the ebb and flow, the ups and downs, but don't really know what to do with it or how to be supportive. Like women, they want things to make sense, and they desire a great relationship. They also don't want to get blamed when they don't know what's going on.

Unfortunately, it is my experience that there is little attempt from men to initiate honest communication to establish understanding. Learning the logical sequence of the female monthly sex cycle, and being willing to get in sync with it, gives a man endless opportunities to participate in co-creating the easy relationship he has always wanted: more sex, more fun, more intelligent connection, more heartfelt safety, and long-term security. Women want the same things, only more *varied* sexuality to match their varied sexual cycle. Sex comes in many different packages and different energy levels, in spite of what we've been taught, or, more correctly, what we haven't been taught.

Society and the Environment

It is vital to understand the feminine cycle as a holistic health tool and a life-long rhythm that regulates life around us, rather than a target for crude jokes, ignorant comments, and accusatory remarks. Women are often patronized and labeled as emotional and unpredictable or, even worse, difficult. This creates prejudice and sometimes dire consequences at home and work. Our cycles have become an eye-winking joke and, because we cycle, we are often blamed for the problems in relationships. It's difficult to be well-rounded as a female when the one thing that fuels our female power core, our feminine cycle, has been reduced to an embarrassing, misunderstood, underground existence.

> What's the best way to dismantle a culture, the honor, and the sovereignty of the people? Take their language.
>
> —Hailana Farden

When the underlying message in our societal consciousness is that women are a problem, we fail to protect them from the varied spectrum of abuses such as domestic violence, lack of equal pay, and denial of sovereignty over one's own body. When we insidiously diminish the female, we tend to diminish the issues we are inclined to *think of* as female, such as the environment, healthcare, homelessness, and hunger (i.e., home and hearth).

The Thread That Binds Us in Unity

Throughout history, over various time periods, lands, and cultures, female power slowly diminished, supplanted by male domination and takeover of things that used to belong to (or should have belonged to) women. Land and personal possessions were no longer the property of the female, thereby reducing female leadership and voice in the community.

Although it would take almost a century and a half for women to gain the right to vote in the United States, and over 200 years *to begin* to receive acceptance as equal partners, women remained in charge

of reproductive issues in general. When this country was founded, menstruation, limiting and controlling family size (including legal abortion[2] and preventative practices using herbs or rhythm awareness), pregnancy, labor, birthing, nursing, menopause, and personal care continued to be the untouchable domain of women, with assistance from (and circles created by) female midwives, herbalists, medicine women, grandmothers, mothers, sisters, and aunties.[3]

By the mid-1800s, the unthinkable and unacceptable occurred: the newly created American Medical Association rapidly began forcing its way into the female reproductive body by replacing female midwives with male doctors,[4] stealing the one thing women rightly had power over—their wombs. A sociological gender rape, if you will.

To make matters worse, male doctors had very little knowledge of the female reproductive system. In his book, *At Home: A Short History of Private Life*, Bill Bryson says, "The inevitable consequence of all this was that ignorance of female anatomy and physiology among medical men was almost medieval." He goes on to explain that they didn't understand women's bodies at all. They had a general belief that simply being a woman was a pathological condition. Bryson wrote, "Menstruation was described in medical texts as if it were a monthly act of willful negligence."[5]

The De-Feminization of the World

No matter where or when in history, once the takeover of the female body was complete and incorporated into society over time, the deed was done: female rule over reproduction was forgotten or no longer acceptable. With the entire female experience and existence now shrouded in shame, the female monthly cycle became a private and unspeakable thing, leaving women isolated from each other and unable to receive the teachings normally handed down in gatherings and oral tradition. The patriarchal arrow of control and destruction hit its bull's eye. We have not yet recovered.

Having nothing left, and no real world of their own except what was allowed or assigned to them, women had no choice but to as-similate into the man's way of doing things in the world. Forced to cut her own umbilical cord and abandon her feminine power core (and therefore her post as the overseer of the health and well-being of the population), it is my personal feeling that energetically, the collective "she" simply checked out, existing outside of her human shell, secretly resenting and dealing with her reproductive body as it inconveniently presented itself. The world was now officially "de-feminized."

> Post–Traumatic Stress Syndrome does not only happen in war, it happens with women in everyday life.
>
> —Judith Thompson

The Danger

Physical, spiritual, and financial muscle are timeless methods of abuse used by husbands, fathers, courts, and clergy to control wives, daughters, and sisters. When women are told it is God's will for men to rule over them, this collective psycho-spiritual grip takes a last-ing hold. Women honor what their men have to say more than they trust their own inner knowing (or voice from God). They back down and comply. When men are told it is God's will and right to rule over women, they often end up hurting them.

When one feels disempowered to optimally navigate her own life, she becomes dependent on her abuser for survival. This leads not only to ill health and endangerment of the female, but to the emo-tional ill health of her children and of our society. Domestic violence and poverty continue to thrive and insult.

Sexual Shadows

It is true that our gender has gained an enormous amount of influence, with growing numbers of women holding high-level positions in high places. However, a strong undercurrent of absolute distrust in women's good moral judgment continues to linger, invade, and pervade—cutting deeply, and at times crushing the day-to-day spirit of even the most seemingly empowered women. Our bodies and minds continue to be exploited and mistreated by both ends of a strangely perverted and grossly dominating spectrum: the *violently* sexual human shadow of sex slavery and extreme pornography, and the *piously* sexual human shadow of extreme religious beliefs.

> How can a woman live her own life if she is not permitted to manage her own body?
>
> —Roberta Mary Pughe & Paula Anema Sohl

Globally, our gender faces such atrocities as martial law, stoning, female genital mutilation, and child marriage, as well as kidnapping and gang rape. Around the world, women and young girls are forced into prostitution, drugs, bondage, and pornography to stay alive. In some countries, professional women are controlled and devalued by having their law degrees or medical licenses declared invalid.[6] Human trafficking (sex slavery) is a colossal industry, not only abroad, but in the U.S. as well.

Atrocities are committed by the same abuser in different cloaks, whether through physical and emotional violence at home, kidnapping young teens for use in the sex industry, or denying reproductive health information and access to healthcare. It's all cruelty, whether we dress it in the obvious (dark, scary, violent) or the insidious (sugary, good, patriotic, family values).

When women are taught that they are not "the boss" of themselves in their own homes and this is a notion supported by other women in their lives, boundaries are non-existent. Confusion about what one can say "yes" or "no" to is the way of life. When women's bodies and souls are vulnerable to the frightening circumstances that surround them, self-determination is diminished and hope is often lost.

> The truth is that male religious leaders have had, and still have, an option to interpret holy teachings either to exalt or subjugate women. They have, for their own selfish ends, overwhelmingly chosen the latter. Their continuing choice provides the foundation or justification for much of the pervasive persecution and abuse of women throughout the world. —Jimmy Carter

Today's woman is a mere shadow of the powerful Feminine, having lost touch with the very thing that fuels her power core: her monthly rhythm. This, in turn, means she's lost her compass for how to live an optimally healthy life, physically, mentally, and soulfully. No longer does she have a pulse on her own being, and therefore she is no longer *in control* of her being. Doctors know best, clergy know best, lawmakers know best, voters know best.

Making a Planetary Shift

As men and women, we have spiraled so far away from our centers that we no longer resemble the healthy model of our design. The male gender, as a global group, has carried forward the combative and dominating force of their natures over their protective and wise natures. Men love the *idea* of being a hero (and it seems nearly every man yearns to be one), but their training to *be* men tends to send them down a different track of machismo, patronization, or no specific rite-of-passage into real maturity.

The female gender, as a global group, is rising to power from their place in a man's world and have learned how to play the man's game to get ahead (without much choice), rather than from the needed and powerful balancing perspective of their core female essence (it's not been allowed). It has been buried for so long that most of us barely know it exists.

The education and empowerment of women throughout the world cannot fail to result in a more caring, tolerant, just, and peaceful life for all.

—Aung San Suu Kyi, Nobel Peace Prize Laureate

War, poverty, abuse, class systems, and extreme political strife are simply reflections of the ugly internal turmoil and disconnection we hold as humans. It is my contention that, in order to resolve our personal and global conflicts, we must make a conscious effort to reconnect with the natural rhythm of our *higher* core gender power.

We must first, individually, become centered and steady in the highest essence of our design, solidly aligned, with our feet on the ground, in the reality of *what is*, and with our heads in conscious awareness of *what can be*. Only in a solid and balanced state of courage, trust, and goodwill toward others can we craft decisions together for the good of all to create a planetary shift so profound that we are able to create the safe and sustainable world we desire.

The day you really want an end to hunger, there will be no more hunger.

—Neale Donald Walsch

Currently, forward-thinking people are making huge adjustments in the societal consciousness, driven by the desire for a more peaceful world. Yet manifesting these ideas into action is a far more sluggish proposition. We like to believe that we no longer have gender issues now that women are "free" to pursue their dreams, so we reject gender inequality as a possible source of our problems. I see it as our number one problem globally. I believe that if we give women their legal sovereignty, equal power, and respect, we will experience a shift so profound that many of our other challenges will simply become non-issues.

Civilization has been a time of constant war, both literally and in the body/mind of humanity. In such conditions, hyper-masculinity and hypo-femininity predominate. Neither gender is served by these extremes—they are meant to be very temporary—crisis modes to endure brief, intense periods of conflict. In our world, they are the norm. Both genders are affected terribly by such conditions, and indeed, if one is affected, the other is equally affected, since they are intimately related through duality polarity.

—Gregg Marchese

Our gender relationships and ways of being will continue to be out of balance as long as our world continues to be run by an old and immature male paradigm; while the female way is tentative and slow to integrate, we are excelling in the business world at a rapid pace.

Throughout this book I ask men to balance *their* end of the scale by stepping into a higher, more mature position of power as men who include and align with women, becoming the true heroes who protect by protecting our rights, and who co-create rather than dominate. This requires a fearless release of control, while trusting and transforming into leaders of integrity who stand tall, serve, and guide. It requires a willingness to synchronize, as much as possible, with the female undulating rhythm and its advantageous importance, and to respect her highly for it.

I am asking women to balance the global scale by tapping into and identifying that same inner wave of their innate knowledge and wisdom; to awaken, surface, and step up to teach their inclusive ways of approaching the world with vision and cooperative leadership; to walk without fear of being one's self; and to align with and trust the New Men who are hearing this call to action. This requires drumming up the courage and confidence to speak in truth and vision without fear of retaliation or rejection. It means catching every moment that you, against your desire, fall into acquiescing, conceding, submitting, complying, or reducing yourself, often out of conditioned habit or fear, even when no overt pressure has been put on you to do so. It means stopping the habit of oppressing *yourself* when you could negotiate and participate.

It requires recalibrating yourself from the inside out, beginning with tuning in to your most primordial rhythm—your monthly hormonal blueprint—and claiming and owning your magnificence and sovereignty.

Far more than biology, the feminine cycle is an *experience*, the one true thread of data that links the *human* source of creation to the *original* universal source of creation, the instruction manual for the human design and that of the Earth Mother planet we live on. Women must surf and refine their rhythms and share this information. In order for the New Man to protect and honor the female way and the environment, he must understand it, get in sync with it, and begin to glean knowledge that helps him uncover his own empowering rhythmic nuances as well.

Declare publicly your gut-level commitment to whatever you decide to do with your one "wild and precious life." Go stand in your power and walk with intention to make it so.

—Gloria Feldt

The New Paradigm

People all over the globe are proposing new thoughts, or combining old ways with new ways, to create this culture of peace. Each individual's gift is another piece to the puzzle, whether focused on conscious economics, new technology, or human behavior. My focus is on personal, gender, and social healing by offering up my take on the source of so much of our disparity—lack of true and real respect for female intellect and capability and equal incorporation of the female way.

In order to untangle and redefine this paradigm, we must examine our social programming to see, comprehend, and acknowledge how we ended up this way so that we don't repeat it. Only then can we truly acknowledge, apologize, forgive, and start anew to rebuild the female psyche. Powerful, loving, and confident is the way she is meant to function. This transformation needs to begin where we all begin—in the guiding rhythm of the sacred womb.

> We never change things by fighting the existing reality. To change something, build a new model that makes the existing model obsolete.
>
> —Buckminster Fuller

Indigenous Ways

Several years ago a man in my town had been traveling and brought back a story about the respect shown to elder women currently living in Yucatan Indian Villages. He said that they carry their staffs when showing up at Council to speak, and from these staffs hang strips of fabric, one strip from every menstrual cloth they have ever worn. When they enter the Council room, all are silenced.

It was explained that these women carry evidence of the blood they shed for their people throughout their lifetimes. Because this blood was not instigated by Man, it represents pure and strong sacrifice that carries more power, more weight, than does blood shed in a man-made war. It is spiritual and primal. It is recognized, seen, and revered by their people. It rules all, above all.

This man deeply regretted the dishonoring that has been going on in our culture for way too long now, for the abandonment of our women—the everyday warriors—in spite of the endless hours they have put in, the love they give, what they endure, and what their bodies go through. He felt shame for those of his gender who choose to dominate and demean rather than see and protect this sacred, exquisite beauty and wisdom. As a people, we have fallen from grace.

Nature and Spirit Alignment

Throughout time and cultures there have been pockets of examples that reflect this same story—of societies where women held power alongside the men. Evidence is easily found through carved images and artifacts before written history, and among ancient and current indigenous peoples such as the Hopi, some South Pacific and Caribbean Islanders, and the Cherokee and the Iroquois. We also find it among ancient and current farming communities, from the prehistoric Neolithic era of 7,000–4,000 B.C. to the hard-working and peaceful hippie-type cooperatives of today. We see the new share-towns cropping up all over the world that are designed to reduce each person's carbon footprint. Blending individual success and freedom with collective consciousness and village conscience, we align with the recycling forces of Nature—a sort of gifting community and entrepreneurial *feng shui*, if you will. The common denominator among all of these cultures is the reverence for the Earth, which in turn seems to give us a tangible connection to spirit and the matrix all around us.

Numerous theories live on regarding the reason for our disconnection from honoring the Earth aspect (and therefore our natural rhythmic awareness), which seems to have coincided with the genesis

The womb is the foundation of a woman, the rich soil and immovable center of silent power that allows the heart to bloom and open safely and fully. It has been covered by fear, betrayal, judgment, ignorance, sexual issues, and the loss/abuse of power. Its wisdom and power have been forgotten by most people and deliberately hidden by others.

—Padma Aon

of dishonoring women. In his book, *The Alphabet Versus the Goddess*, Leonard Shlain offers his observation that when written language replaced oral tradition, it triggered the left hemispheres of our brains to dominate our actions, changing human priorities and focus from an ability to see the big picture and connect all things to one that breaks the focus into parts.[7]

There is also a growing theory that points to the *privatization* of our Earth land as being the biggest culprit of our economic challenges of today, and the inability of all humans to have access to natural, Source-given land resources for survival, creating particularly disastrous results for women. In his essay, "The Problem of the Modern World," John Mohawk states, "When land became a 'commodity' and lost its status as provider and sustainer of life, Western civilization began its history of subjugation and exploitation of the Earth and Earth-based cultures."

> The historical process of enclosures that privatized land formerly open to common usage in England and Europe forced people off the land and into the cities, where work began to become available as industrialism arose. Women had a central role in managing how the commons were used, which gave them an important economic role that they carried off quite competently in close harmony with their men and the community as a whole. Enclosures stripped women of this crucial role and, since they were not allowed employment in the cities alongside their men, they lost all practical economic role and power. Thus it appeared that women had no practical knowledge when it was they who had the most practical role of all, enhanced by their heart and intuitional abilities. All they had left was their bodies, and that is what they sold to make a living. Hi ho, the derry o!   —Wendell Fitzgerald

Addressing a crowd at Amherst College in 2001, Alanna Hartzog stated, "The European indigenous women were strong and clear wild women with equal status to their men. They could stand their ground because they had access to the common lands. The imperial forces called them witches. Women who practiced healing and agriculture, who had their own lands and were leaders of their communities, were tortured, hanged, or burned at the stake. The Holy Inquisition was a women's holocaust; about 85 percent of those killed were women. I consider this to be the most significant story of the past two thousand years for women of European descent."[8]

Ancient Whisperings

We feel the loss of this pure, elevated honor of women, and many people worldwide are making efforts to bring it back. Ceremonies, prayers, and events are gaining speed to raise the consciousness of the planet by helping us to tap into this sacred "equal respect" of genders and "remember" it. We are doing our best to access the lost and oppressed information of our ancestors—from a time when women were truly respected (without domination) and men had true honor (without dominating).

We are trying to retrieve a type of wisdom that is much more than a memory. We are summoning the return of our deeper souls to embody our elevated, realized gender lineage. We are reaching into history to seek out our wisest grandmothers and grandfathers of long ago to speak to us through our DNA. We seek the graceful richness of our muses, our gender mentors. We yearn to know the deeply suppressed knowledge and wisdom within the Feminine psyche, free from the fog of rationalization and depleting compromise. We beckon the mature Masculine, our hunky, wise hero, to return and challenge the bullying mentality that has run the world for centuries.

Most of us desire to live in a loving and kind world, free of global or domestic terrorists who threaten our lives and liberties. We wish to travel, participate in the spiritual practice of our choice *or not*, and have access to medical services, all in peace and safety. We'd like to see that all people have food, shelter, and clean water. We want to know, above all, that our children are safe at home or school, at work or at play. I want to allow my daughter to be out with friends or travel the world without me worrying about the worst.

We aspire to embrace humanity with confidence, enthusiasm, and master knowledge; to fully engage with our sexual partners with true desire, passion, and devotion while receiving the same in return; to

Our written languages, particularly those that are alphabetic, have allowed humans to abstract themselves out of the world, the Earth, and have set themselves to be over the Earth to exploit it. They have lost connection to the natural intelligence of the Earth—a connection that is more present when only an oral language is the mainstay of the culture, as in indigenous peoples.

—Torrey Byles

like ourselves; to fit in with others and fit perfectly with another; to love our bodies, expand our thoughts, and be loved and accepted for who we are; *to belong*. To fill this tall order, we must first *belong* to *ourselves*, to be in touch with the natural and spiritual rhythms of our own unique identities and natures.

Buried Treasure

When Native Americans were forced off the land on this continent, they buried many of their sacred ceremonial pieces in order to pro-tect them—so that they would not be denigrated or destroyed. Gran-ite bowls were turned upside-down along riverbeds to look like rocks. *Burying* these pieces actually kept the ceremonies *alive* by cloaking them in protection, spiritually trusting (or innately knowing) that these items needed to go underground until the medicine people or "wisdom keepers" of the future could retrieve them. Once in safe hands, the new guardian is guided to sit in meditative ceremony to reveal the purpose and meaning of a sacred artifact as well as instruc-tions on how to use it in ceremony once again.

Each woman is the Wisdom Keeper of her own sacred vessel, her treasured womb—the *human* source of creation, which contains the buried feminine cycle blueprint—the original *and* ever-evolving Feminine insight; woman's unbounded potential, magnanimous influence, and royalty—*Womb Wisdom*. It's a carefully packaged time capsule, an instruction manual, a treasure map. Like a message in a bottle, the collective womb has rhythmically bounced around in unfriendly waters without breaking, surviving on auto-pilot until the turbulent, dominating time passes. Once landed on the shore of a safe and welcoming environment, with the cooperation and protection of the Masculine, the confined contents buried deep within the uncon-scious layer of each female psyche can be uncorked and released.

It seems that leaders across time and space have understood that whoever owns the sacred vessel owns the women, or conversely, who-ever owns the women, owns the sacred vessel. If they own the sacred vessel, they own the human race and the genetic influence of it. They are drawn to its miraculous power—the ability to give life. It is the human Holy Grail, the water-that-turns-into-wine every month, the blood-of-the-Divine chalice, the salt water from which all souls are baptized into the human experience. They are drawn to the glory of capturing and conquering the mystery.

Great efforts have been made and strategies devised to control the instructions and rules over this holy treasure, but all of these attempts have been in vain. Females may be subjugated and oppressed and the womb vessel battered and scarred from this internment, but the fact remains that the secrets are something no one else will ever possess. The woman is the only one who can decipher the mysterious code, *because it is her own personal code.*

Like any good mystery, the evidence is right in front of us, in plain sight. The set of instructions from the *Source* of the Universe is directly embedded and intricately woven throughout the entire fabric of each female's physical, mental, and emotional operating systems, serving as her guiding light for optimal function, as long as she doesn't forsake her own authority over it or reject its importance.

Womb Wisdom

Within us lives the womb, the epicenter of bonding—the sacred temple of creation—the original home to all human beings. The womb (or, if removed, the remembered chamber) is the loving holding vessel where creating, nurturing, bonding, growing, and recycling take place.

> All of us come from the primordial womb from which life was created. Dark, endless, and compassionate, it is the pregnant potential of life itself. Because it is the genesis for all possibilities, it is the doorway to healing and awakening. When you allow yourself to experience this energetic womb, you discover complete, limitless love and acceptance. It is here in its still, quiet love that you awaken to your light. —Misa Hopkins

The womb is the ultimate model for connecting and transforming. This safe, internal holding vessel, ruler of the night and influenced by the rhythmic Moon, is quintessential, right brain Feminine energy: receptive, compassionate, wise, and big pictured; all knowing, inclusive, and connected. It is equally as potent as the exposed external expression, ruler of the day, influenced by the steady Sun: the quintessential left brain Masculine energy, which is action-oriented, moving light, and dissected; focused and exclusive. Developed and nurtured in the warmth of the female's womb during gestation, both energies are represented by the left and right hemispheres of *every* human's brain, creating a balanced gender intelligence in the psyche and soul of every male and female. Although each gender accesses the hemispheres differently, this Womb Wisdom, the ability to transform, heal, grow, and fully connect, lives inside *each and every one of us.*

The hand that rocks the cradle rules the world.

—William Ross Wallace

Yet, because we are wired to carry and sway with the womb's rhythmic blueprint throughout our lives, the power and greatest understanding of this wisdom belongs to the women. We are the walking embodiment of this sacred text, the instruction manual for being compassionate and healthy humans; a fractal rhythm of the Universe so powerful it contains dark *and* light, resting *and* action, building *and* purging; a wavy recycling system for our bodies, minds, and emotions.

The New Medicine Woman

Your female wisdom and gifts are the medicine needed to balance and heal the many challenges we experience in our world. Today, environmentally and socially, our distressed world needs each woman to wake from her slumber, reclaim her vessel, and retrieve the wisdom code that our female ancestors protectively buried so long ago. It is ours to teach, emanate, and illuminate.

In Search of Our Hero: The Male Rhythm

Is it possible that synchronizing with the sacred text within the female is the *complete* and *balanced* answer to our many global challenges? What sacred text do the men embody? What medicine is the male responsible for bringing forth to humanity and meant to express? Surely war and domination are not the paths of the spiritual warrior. By tapping into the kindhearted stillness of the Womb Wisdom within them, it is time for men to begin to decipher their own hidden code and bring it to light. Until we truly understand the rich healing properties within the longer rhythmic blueprint of the Masculine, we must follow the female.

Sacred Alignment

The ancient rhythm of our design lives in alignment with the natural and spiritual forces of the Universe. By digging deeply within us we can discover and uncover the interconnected root system of our divinity. Here lies the inner beauty and life force of the *human* species—the Divine or Sacred Feminine; our Sleeping Beauty, inside each of us waiting to be awakened.

2. Universal Rhythms

The Female Rhythm & Living in Sync with Nature

The patterns that reveal themselves in our lives and our being-ness can be seen in the patterns of Nature, the cycles, the structures of life, and are often reflections, mirror images, of what is around us.

—Jane Hardwicke Collings

Rhythms, Phases, Waves, & Patterns

We find rhythms, patterns, cycles, phases, and waves in every aspect of Nature. From the food chain order, migration of whales and birds, high and low tides, tree dormancy and fruit production, to ever-changing cloud movement, weather temperatures, and our orbiting solar system, Mother Nature is one voluptuous, organically pulsating body functioning within a pulsating Universe. She is a well-oiled machine, with each living thing connected to all others. From human bodies down to the strangest-looking microscopic bugs, life is designed for survival and function, and forms a complex weave of systems within systems. Each system is part of the team and any change from one is going to affect the others. It is important to discuss rhythms in Nature for a deeper and richer understanding of the rhythms within the female monthly cycle.

> All life is interrelated. We are all caught in an inescapable network of mutuality tied in a single garment of destiny. Whatever affects one directly affects all indirectly.
>
> —Martin Luther King, Jr.

The Source

I think we can all agree that Nature is not man-made. Its seen and unseen forces were created by either "Master *Science*" or a "Master *Scientist*," whichever you prefer. The more we align with these natural forces, the closer we get to this original Source. Nature is the direct expression and voice of Source available to us all without a middleman, the pure form or intention of the *master blueprint*, *instruction manual*, or *correct flow* for all living things, reflected in large and small rhythms.

Only by tapping into and living in sync with the natural, rhythmic forces of our bodies, the environment, and the Universe, will we be in sync with Source, unlocking the vast knowledge of this higher intelligence, thus elevating our collective intelligence. When we don't take care of Nature or the natural eco-systems of our planet and our bodies, we are going against the brilliance of Source, where all the answers lie.

Sacred Geometry

We find not only rhythms, waves, and cycles in the natural world, we find patterns of squares, circles, spheres, triangles, orbits, and spirals, replicating themselves over and over. For instance, spirals can be found on the tiniest *and* largest of seashells, in river whirlpools, flowers, and galaxies. Spheres can be found in water bubbles, seed pods, and planets. The Universe is the macrocosm, with an endless number of microcosms—miniatures—of rhythms and patterns within it. This is Sacred Geometry.

Ocean waves, radio waves, hair waves, hormone fluctuation, and flags waving in the wind all give a similar impression.

On his website, The Geometry Code, author Bruce Rawles explains this phenomenon as an "inseparable relationship of the part to the whole," describing it as a "principle of oneness." He goes on to say, "This principle of interconnectedness, inseparability, and union provides us with a continuous reminder of our relationship to the whole, a blueprint for the mind, to the sacred foundation of all things created."

Earth Rhythms

Earth is a living, active planet within an active solar system. Because of this, each living thing has its own biological clock ticking away. So even when dormant, outside influences and growth move the clock along until one phase succumbs to another, one action is overtaken by another. Each system cycles with a rhythm that reaches a height of activity and then reverses until it reaches a resting phase, in order to reboot or regenerate to gain energy and begin again. All plants and animals are systems with various growth patterns and rhythms like this. Some cycles are predictable, repeating in a fairly stable pattern, while other cycles are unique and unpredictable, completely dependent on outside variables to determine their duration.

We can find as much peace and beauty in the minuscule center of one flower as in the extensive nebula of a distant galaxy. —Eric Alan

The Four Seasons Cycle

One of the main cycles we humans can relate to and are connected with is the four seasons. It's not the fact that the seasons are dictated by the Earth orbiting around the Sun, it's the fact that we *feel and experience* each season. They *affect us* and our everyday lives. We launch into one season after another with excitement and anticipation, settle in to enjoy or endure it, and then gear up for the next one. We make sure, for instance, that we plant our gardens early in Spring (if there is no frost), because we know the roots of the plants must be established to handle and reap the benefits of the Summer heat. By the end of Summer we prepare for Fall, the end of another growing season and the beginning of the new school term. Winter is spent connecting with loved ones and taking action on creative projects. We know that when Spring hits, we'll want to be outside again.

Compassion, the Buddha taught, comes from understanding impermanence, transience, flow, how one thing passes into another, how everything and everyone is connected.

—*The Buddha: The Story of Siddhartha*

Natural Instinct

Indigenous cultures naturally incorporated cyclic forces into daily life for survival, navigating by the stars, Summer and Winter homeland, raising crops, daily productivity and rest, hunting, gathering, and birthing babies. Knowing what part of the plant to pick, and when, was crucial for utilizing its healing properties and possibly made the difference between life and death. We continue to carry this ancient survival wisdom within us.

The Natural World

Natural Rhythm Principles are truths about repeated patterns of fundamental cycles, rhythms, energy flow, and Sacred Geometry, as well as cause and effect. Natural Rhythm Principles are the seen and unseen mathematical processes, or delivery systems, of Source. They fuel and inspire our ways of being—from our physical, emotional, and soul bodies, to our environments, businesses, and relationships. When we mindfully incorporate Natural Rhythm Principles into our day-to-day lives, we naturally find ourselves feeling serene and connected without thinking about it. This is *love*, and when we feel surrounded by it, things seem to go smoothly, doors open wide, and motivation directs us to find innovative and peaceful solutions. Natural Rhythm Principles tap into our own wells of self-love, then that same love is reflected back to others. Source feels present, or within reach.

Our Perfect Design

The human body is full of Sacred Geometry examples—microcosmic systems of divine relationships within our Universe. In his writings, the Roman architect Vitruvius suggested that religious temples should be designed after the proportions of the human body because it is the model of perfection. In his "Vitruvian Man," Leonardo da Vinci shows us the perfection Vitruvius had in mind. When we allow our natural systems to align with universal natural rhythms, our bodies function according to the way they were designed.

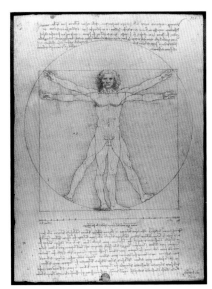

Our Living Spaces

Architects have long imitated Nature with their inventive and geometrically shaped building designs. Icons such as Frank Lloyd Wright incorporated the organic flow of the surrounding landscape *with* the indoor living space for maximum function, beauty, well-being, and with respect for the local land and culture. Just looking at his designs brings a sense of peace to the viewer.

Seasonal, Rhythmic Eating

Depending on where one lives and food availability, there has been a resurgence to eat *rhythmically*—whatever is in season locally—instead of eating the same way throughout the year, by replacing frozen or canned foods shipped in from someplace else with freshly picked fruits and vegetables. The reasoning behind this resurgence is twofold: we get the intended nutrients when eating fresh rather than processed food, and our bodies are more likely to be getting what they need for staying healthy in the specific environment where we live. Eating a well-rounded diet from our gardens and communities keeps our bodies in a check-and-balance mode.

> Man's heart away from Nature becomes hard. Lack of respect for growing, living things soon led to lack of respect for humans, too.
>
> —Chief Luther Standing Bear

Out of Sync with Natural Rhythm Principles

When we don't incorporate Nature and her rhythms into our living spaces and day-to-day lives, we are ultimately going against Source. We don't feel well physically, mentally, or emotionally, and don't know why. We often end up making poor decisions for ourselves, our families, and our environment.

Environmental Challenges: Our Medicinal Rainforests

One glaring *environmental* example where we as a global community do not live in communion with Nature is our lack of awareness of rainforest importance. By slowly destroying our rainforests we are slowly destroying the quality of living on our own planet home. Once covering 12 percent of the planet, these biologically diverse regions now cover less than five percent due to land clearing for timber sales and cattle, ruining the soil and destroying approximately 50,000 plant, animal, and insect species every year. Often thought of as the "Lungs of the Planet," the Amazon Rainforest produces 20 percent of our Earth's oxygen (by converting carbon dioxide into oxygen), regulates our global weather and rainfall, sustains 50 percent of the species on Earth, and provides 70 percent of our known cancer-preventing plant-medicines. Yet we still somehow opt for bulldozing the land for a short-sighted quick sale, *permanently* killing off the very resources with which *Source* has designed to heal us when we are ill.

> The vine was red and layered throughout, resembling the female uterine membrane. I was always amazed at Nature's way of letting us know what a plant might be used for by matching the color or shape with the complaint. I had noticed that this relationship between color and use seemed most evident when it came to plants connected to women's needs.
>
> —Rosita Argivo

We seem to fail to see that when we cut the life force of our planet's body, we cut the available life-giving properties that are meant to sustain our human bodies and the cause-and-effect matrix of all living things. Sometimes our web-of-life can adjust and compensate, and sometimes it cannot; some things are lost forever.

Human Challenges: The Female Womb

The most glaring *human* example of where we as a global community do not live in sync with Nature is in the tiny, individual eco-system safely stored within each and every woman for all or part of her life. Cradled by bones and humility, rocked by wisdom and spirit, the female womb is the *nest* from which all of human life flows. When we disregard it, we disregard all of humankind.

When we treat it as a disjointed embarrassment, acknowledge only pieces and parts of it, and call women the worst of names for it, we fail to see this small and mighty rhythm as the core of female health and well-being, and therefore the core of *all* human health and well-being. This multi-layered, holistic tool is a major puzzle

When you're deeply connected to your blood cycle, you're deeply connected to the Earth's cycle.

—Jaya Opela

piece of the larger social and communal rhythms. When it is "off," everything is thrown off. It is crucial to understand that if negativity is cast at the womb and its rhythm, negativity will lie in it, emanate from it, and extend beyond it, rippling out from *everything* the female thinks and does and produces from it. This rhythm must be given optimal reverence in order for our children to start out in an optimal environment.

> We can ask what the return of the Great Mother would contribute to healing our currently impaired comprehension of the Earth as the sacred giver and sustainer of life. —Osprey Orielle Lake

The feminine rhythm is designed to extend a loving and positive flow by the woman and the humans she produces. It has been disrupted by the disrespect toward it and the takeover and assault of it by others. When the sacred wisdom of it is smothered and conquered, dishonored and put to sleep, going against the organic flow of Nature and the natural rhythm of the Universe (the voice and the manifestation of Source), the population becomes socially deficient, imbalanced, and unhealthy.

You are a microcosm
of the Universe.

—Jean Houston

Human Rhythms

Our Universe, planet, ecosystems, human bodies, and the systems inside of our bodies are all naturally compatible members of a rhythmic network, yet we tend to identify and address them separately. It's time to "re-member" these rhythms in order to once again tap into Nature—Source's "alignment" solution for ideal function and flow. The actions of one affect all.

Physical

Our human bodies, being yet another ecosystem within the larger natural forces of the Universe, also have all kinds of rhythmic cycling going on within them—usually going from active to slowing way down to active again. When sitting perfectly still, our hearts are still beating, our blood circulating, our cells dividing, and our food digesting. Our brain waves go from stages of deep sleep (in order for the body to reboot or regenerate) to meditative to moderately active and then to very active. Studies are showing that our brains process information most efficiently when we are at rest.[9]

Our muscles are a good example of this. We have a tendency to think that we are building muscle when we are working out, when in fact the opposite is true: "The actual building of muscles takes place not during a strenuous workout, but during the recovery period following the workout," says my personal trainer Don Chasey.

The more we understand the wisdom of the patterns and rhythms by which our own bodies abide, the more in charge of our own health we'll be. We must be our own best health advocates, because the medical profession often seems slow to catch up to what it is we need or already "see" that we need. Getting in tune with what harmonizes our bodies will harmonize our souls and relationships. Once this is in place, our individually unique gifts will begin to surface: the truth of who we are and what we have to offer to the world.

Seeing beauty in a flower could awaken humans, however briefly, to the beauty that is an essential part of their own innermost being, their true nature.

—Eckhart Tolle

Emotional-Response Body

In the same way that the *physical* body system cycles in and out in rhythmic motion, the *emotional-response* body cycles in and out as well. This body of emotional responses can create a physical reaction of feeling healthy or ill, and the reverse can be true as well: physical health can create a situation of balanced or imbalanced emotion. Either way, they work interdependently, with one affecting the other.

Our emotional and physical experiences trigger thoughts (and vice versa). The vibes that emanate from us when we think, speak, and take action affects everything and everyone around us, eventually affecting the entire world experience. One action, or inaction, always sets something else into motion within ourselves and has an impact on all of our interactions.

Communal Thoughts and Time Periods

A yoga teacher I had in the 1970s taught our class about time periods during which the higher collective consciousness tends to be particularly magnetic. Out of the status quo of everyday thinking comes new, or remembered, ideas—mind-blowing creativity or a form of passionate humanity that changes the course of the world's direction. Until, that is, we take it for granted and let it slip through our hands, allowing darker, threatening forces to tear down the infrastructure of our beautiful masterpiece of hope and exhilaration. Thus society seems to ebb and flow over time between expansive and constrictive thought.

From the arising of this, comes the arising of that.
—Buddha

Our thoughts and actions influence how others think until an energetic gang mentality is formed, whether the actual thoughts, feelings, and actions make any logical sense or not. Individuals *do* make a difference, but they too must influence others in order to gather enough thoughts and actions to create a "gang" that can overtake the current way of doing things. How we think *collectively* affects our personal, family, community, and global tastes such as what we wear, how we entertain ourselves, and what innovations rise to the surface. It also exposes our problem-solving tactics, guides our economy, how often we go to war, and who eats and who does not. This *collective* emotional rhythm shows its high point at times of seeing, hearing, and understanding others who are different from us and its low point at instances of distrust, battle, and human-rights abuses.

Sun & Moon Rhythms

The light and gravitational pull of the Sun and Moon rhythms and cycles have enormous influence over all living things on Earth, including humans, regulating our internal organs and processes and providing us with predictable blueprints to follow daily, monthly, and yearly, for our physical and emotional well-being. The more we understand how these rhythms affect us, the more power we'll have over our own health and well-being.

Natural Light: An Endangered Component

Electricity is a natural by-product of a natural source and harnessed by evolved intelligence and ingenuity, but humans have used it to create an artificial world. Although the Sun and Moon certainly continue to lift our spirits when they are in their glory and have a tendency to make us feel down when they are hidden, our male and female bodies do *not easily tell the difference* between the seasons because we no longer cycle *naturally* and *consistently* by these light rhythms, which are crucial components to healthy human living.

Living indoors more and more with forced air and heating, lamps and overhead lighting, computer screens, and other electronics have confused our biological cues, creating new signals to keep our full body systems functioning and surviving. We have spun ourselves away from our naturally rhythmic centers, lingering outside of our own bodies, trying to figure them out and not really relating to them, instead of living *inside* of them and in conjunction with the Earth. Most people I talk to have little to no idea of what their bodies are doing, or supposed to be doing, at any given time of the day, month, or year for optimal health. We are taught that it needs to be the same all the time.

The good news is that it appears that the Sun is far more powerful than artificial lighting and that it continues to affect us; we need to learn as much as possible about the natural rhythm of the Sun, while factoring in our disruption of this rhythm with artificial lighting.

Concerns about our extreme climate conditions, polluted water, cancer epidemics, obesity, diabetes, genetically modified foods, and healthcare costs finally have us expanding our consciousness to focus our awareness on cause and effect, and what we can do individually to improve our state of being and our connectedness to our internal and external environments. We now know enough about natural rhythms for health practitioners, fitness coaches, and nutritionists to discuss Natural Rhythm Health with their clients while creating action plans that align with these rhythms. We should be encouraging everyone to turn off artificial lighting more often and expose ourselves to natural lighting as much as possible. Women of reproductive age in particular can benefit from understanding their monthly *and* daily rhythms—dual rhythms that affect their health and well-being.

Three things
cannot long
be hidden:
the Sun,
the Moon,
and the Truth.

—Confucius

The Daily Sun Rhythm

The Circadian Rhythm (*circa*, meaning "about" or "around," and *dian* meaning "day"), also called the 24-hour Body Clock, shows us that living things respond to the same 24-hour rhythm in tandem with the Earth's rotation. Time lapse photography shows us the opening and closing of flowers during a 24-hour cycle. Human body functions such as blood pressure, brain waves, temperature, clotting, male testosterone levels, and pulse consistently ebb and flow according to this cyclical timetable, as well. These rhythms are not learned behaviors. They are hard-wired into cells, tissues, and organs.

Our sleep, digestion, sex drive, overall energy, and hormonal fluctuations and assimilations are now known to individually come alive and shut down at different times of the day and night. For example, as night turns into day, heart rate and blood pressure speed up in anticipation of increased physical activity and slow down when it is time to sleep. Thus it is important to note that rhythm should be considered when administering medications.[10] Initially this recurring pattern was thought to originate in certain cells of the brain or adrenal glands. *We now know that the light of the Sun rules all life on the planet.*

The Sun gives us a daily and seasonal blueprint to follow for optimal health, but man-made lighting allows us to stay up all night if we'd like. Benjamin Franklin's motto, "Early to bed and early to rise, makes a man [or woman] healthy, wealthy, and wise," is based on the idea that rising with the sunlight and going to bed soon after sundown creates a healthy and efficient (and therefore prosperous) human experience.

The Sun reaches its full amount of light energy on the Summer

Solstice and its least amount of light energy on the Winter Solstice in the northern hemisphere. Studies are showing that men's rhythms follow the Sun in two ways: their testosterone levels rise and fall in the same pattern daily[11] as well as intensify or decrease with a 90-day pattern of four seasons in *one year*. Both of these rhythms, daily and seasonally, result in a steadier "burn" as opposed to the undulating monthly pattern of the woman. Just as the Sun rules the day, the year, and men, the Moon rules the night, the month, and women.

The Moon Rhythm and the Monthly Feminine Cycle

It is said that women used to cycle directly with the light of the Moon and all together, starting their Periods on or around the New Moon and ovulating (as well as birthing babies) on the Full Moon (although many women were exactly opposite from this). Oral history from indigenous tribes teaches us that women gathered in groups, in various forms of "Moon Lodges," where they shared female time together.

However, if this is the case, women were cycling every 29 to 30 days, rather than 28. Since the Moon rotates and also orbits around an orbiting and rotating Earth, AND the Earth is orbiting around the Sun, calculating the Moon is trickier than it seems. Everything is spinning in one direction. It's really quite astounding, and it takes some concentration to understand it.

It takes the Moon just under 28 days to complete one full cycle around the Earth and end up back at the place in the sky where it began, relative to the stars. This is called a sidereal month. But because the Earth is also orbiting around the Sun, the Moon has to travel past its original starting point relative to the stars to reach the place where *we on Earth* saw the Moon's cycle begin relative to the Sun. This is called a synodic month. So, if a woman is guided by the light of the Moon only, and begins bleeding on the New Moon, then her Period would come every 29 to 30 days—a couple of days past a full sidereal circle.

It is probable that, once man-made lighting stepped in, our primal reproductive bodies simply adjusted to completing the cycle, the Moon's revolutions around the Earth, and therefore averaged 28 days. Without the navigational guidance of the *moonlight*, our cycles still seem to be influenced in some way—perhaps guided by the cellular memory of natural moonlight.

> The terms "menstruation" and "menses" come from the Latin *mensis* (month), which in turn relates to the Greek *mene* (Moon) and to the roots of the English words month and Moon—reflecting the fact that the Moon also takes close to 28 days to revolve around the Earth (actually 27.32 days). The synodic lunar month, the period between two New Moons (or Full Moons), is 29.53 days long.
> —Nightlighting and the Moon, www.Wikipedia.org

Birth control pills are designed to set our cycles at 28 days, and the medical industry calculates our Periods and Ovulations by a 28-day calendar. It would be so much easier for women to be in tune with their cycles if our culture went by a 13-month calendar of 28 days each. This amounts to 364 days in a year with one "extra" day.

In the same way that the Moon excites or doesn't excite us, our female sex and energy cycles excite or don't excite us. Naturally, when divided into four weeks, the female sex cycle mimics the four phases of the Moon, with a resting phase, a building phase, a manifestation phase, a deconstructing phase, and then back to the resting phase, where it starts all over again.

Week 1: Like the dark New Moon, we are quiet and internal during this phase of *our* cycle.

Week 2: The Waxing Moon's light beginning to shine corresponds with our hormones heightening. We become more *interested* and eventually more *interesting*.

Week 3: The Full Moon can be magnificent in its beauty and reverence. It lights up the land in order for us to be out in it throughout the night, participating in all its grandeur. Full Moon represents Ovulation, the height of our sex drive. *We* are magnificent and stunning at this time.

Week 4: The light energy of the Waning Moon diminishes until it reaches the end of its cycle, where it will once again rest by going dark. The same goes for women: as our hormones tank, we begin to go within ourselves.

Just like the Moon, our hormones adjust every single day, for a full cycle of approximately 28 days. We're simply not the same person every day. Our personalities don't change, but our mindsets *do*, ever so slightly. And just as the Moon affects the ocean tides, constant hormonal changes affect a woman's state of being and what she extends to the world. Sometimes she recedes and exposes her shells on the beach, other times she arrives as a massive monster wave of energy. It is beautiful, intense, passionate, and freeing! Just like the ocean's high and low tides, this female sequence is logical and predictable. Learning to surf it is invigorating and empowering.

Despite all of this we do not treat the feminine cycle like a cycle at all, or even as a rhythm, in the way that we do the Moon or the four seasons, when we greet each phase with interest and anticipation. Over time we have consolidated and reduced the menses to a group of negative, isolated events of PMS and the Period. We don't even acknowledge it correctly. We say we are "cycling" when we are on our Periods. We are "cycling" ALL THE TIME, every day! We just happen to be in the bleeding or purging *phase* of our cycle when we're on our Periods. All phases are interesting and important.

The Feminine Rhythm

In the same way that the Sun regulates high and low energy points throughout a day and the Moon regulates high and low points throughout a month, the female hormonal rhythm signals a woman to lie low or to get moving, to communicate now or to be in seductive or receiving mode; when to eat lightly and when to exercise heavily.

Everything you do today, both physically and mindfully, will be reflected in how you feel tomorrow and next week. When you learn to tap into what is happening with your hormones on a week-to-week and then on a day-to-day basis, and observe how they affect your being, you will begin to understand how to influence them, and will therefore have a better handle on your life and your relationships.

Like the Universe, the human body is one big mathematical equation, with smaller rhythms mimicking bigger forces in Nature. It takes recognizing this "relationship of the parts to the whole" to see the beauty, purpose, and importance of a smaller, yet critical-to-the-whole-world system such as the monthly feminine cycle. Because this core rhythm fuels the female being, the human source of creation, it is most likely *the mightiest source of natural spiritual energy and inspiration on the planet*, and it is spread out every few feet in households over the entire globe.

If we know when a cycle begins and the pattern that it follows, then we also know where and how it will end. Perhaps most important, if we know the conditions that a cycle brings, then we also know what to expect each time it reappears.

—Gregg Braden

The Feminine Cycle Blueprint

Our feminine cycle is about *reproduction*, or *producing*, is it not? It is the productive part of our physical beings. Your entire monthly cycle shows you how to produce more than just babies. If you follow the blueprint of your own unique rhythm, it will show you how to live a fuller and more *productive* and *creative* life in general. The feminine cycle is not just a physical manifestation of being a woman; it is a multi-dimensional tool for showing you your intellectual, spiritual, and physical energy rhythms as well. It will show you how to produce your *life* efficiently.

The goal of 4s4w is for you to master your hormones by understanding that you are a little different each day of your 28-day cycle, and to become aware of what each day or week requires in order to optimize and center your energy so that you can feel better, think better, look better, and relate better.

This blueprint is several cycles in one:

ᔕ Sex Cycle

ᔕ Physical Energy Cycle

ᔕ Communication Cycle

ᔕ Mental Rejuvenation Cycle

ᔕ Beauty Cycle

Each of these cycles moves through the phases together, yet reveals its own pattern, which compliments the others. Each cycle will pass through each archetypal stage of Queen, Visionary, Artist, Builder, Fun Date, Lover, Goddess, Wise Woman, World Leader, Athlete, Fire Walker, and Monk.

This blueprint is a recycling machine! In the same way that garden soil needs to be tilled, turned, planted, and harvested, the fertile soil of our rhythm needs to be recycled continually to produce the best results for our own well-being. A blueprint is a set of instructions, and Mother Nature did not fail to show us the intricacies of this most important design. It is up to us to bring it to the surface to understand and follow. When we experience and comprehend the strengths and

One stereotyped view of women portrays us all as creatures at the mercy of our hormones. "Balls (or should it be ovaries?) to that!" I say. Our hormones undoubtedly have a huge influence on our lives, but there is no reason why we have to become slaves to them. The more we understand how hormones can affect the female body, mind, and emotions, the better able we will be to minimize their negative effects and enhance their positive ones.

—Gillian Rice, GP

weaknesses of each phase, we are better equipped to use this knowledge to our benefit to make certain decisions at certain times, when possible. When we feel good and have energy, there is nothing we can't achieve for ourselves and the betterment of the world.

Summary: The Planetary Circulatory System

Natural rhythms are the circulatory systems of the Universe, so all rhythms must be allowed to flow well for the maximum health of its inhabitants. No different from the human body, these rhythms within the universal body are interconnected and are a support system of the entire operation. If we clog an artery, we can cause a universal heart attack, or live in a state of chronic global ill-health.

Dominance over and disregard for natural rhythms has caused humans to be disconnected, with disastrous results. Believing we are better than and separate from the environment is depleting our natural resources, creating a crisis so dire that it is unknown whether we can reverse the damage. This same arrogance sent the female monthly rhythm underground for women to deal with on their own while being socially persecuted for their management of it. Our world cannot function at its best without the full, loving expression and wise counsel of the Authentic Female. It is time to turn our attention to these deep rhythms with respect for their brilliance. We are one and the same. Understanding the significance of the female rhythm in relation to the unity of science, spirit, and human existence could be the key to finding new solutions for our most challenging global problems.

Suggestions

- Notice the natural changes going on outside your home and workplace. Look at the variation of color and pattern in the leaves. What flowers are closed up in the mornings, yet open up during the day? Listen. When are birds active and then quiet? Become conscious of what you've shut out over time, especially if you spend your time in technological surroundings, and make a commitment to wake up to the natural world around you.

- Our bodies have active, ongoing rhythms of high and low energy phases on a daily, monthly, yearly, and lifetime basis. Jot down the many personal body rhythms you are aware of: day-to-day, month-to-month, year-to-year, or perhaps throughout each day. For instance, coffee serves me better in the afternoon than in the morning, or, I do my best writing in the early morning hours. Stop yourself from eating late, for instance, when your digestion is at a resting phase. Begin to make notes about your feminine cycle, and experiment with the times you go to bed and get up.

- Notice your thoughts and what they prompt you to do. Are they healthy rhythms or destructive habits? Are they love-based or fear-based? Are they poisonous thoughts toward someone else? What is your reaction to the feminine cycle? If you make jokes about it, how do you think that affects women and, ultimately, the world?

- Open your curtains and turn off lights during the day. Live by the natural sunlight flooding through your windows as much as possible. Use your sunglasses only when necessary and let the light enter through your eyes. Allow your body to make needed vitamin D from this energy.

3. Primal Rhythms

The Female Rhythm & the Land of Milk and Honey

I, with a deeper instinct, choose a man who compels my strength, who makes enormous demands on me, who does not doubt my courage or my toughness, who does not believe me naive or innocent, who has the courage to treat me like a woman.

—Anais Nin

Primal Beings

The female body is loaded with sexual connections, an intricate network of triggers and responders designed to prepare the woman for conception, pregnancy, birthing, nursing, and recovery, if needed. On its own, our body's pure, animalistic instinct that lives in the survival *now* could have an endless string of pregnancies, miscarriages, infant deaths, or rambunctious children over an approximately 40-year span of our reproductive fertility. This way, our bodies can kick into production mode if the population count becomes dangerously low for the human culture to survive on the planet. It's a capability we possess.

The male sexual hormones have no need to prepare a uterus for pregnancy every month, so they don't fluctuate as rapidly. As primal beings, they maintain a high libido in order to be ready at any time to fertilize an egg should she beckon him to maintain the population of the village.

Obviously, women and men are more than breeding animals. We are no more meant to spend our lives solely breeding and birthing than we are meant to walk the Earth naked, gathering berries without the hope of cooking creatively with fire.

What is meant to be used *in conjunction* with our physical reproduction tools is our mighty human brain with its ability to reason, plan ahead, invent, and balance our conditions with these same skills. Within this scientific mind are infinite layers of conscious and unconscious imprinted wisdom and memory, along with receptive sensors and intuitive communication skills that seem capable of crossing the room, crossing a country, or crossing into what we think of as spiritual dimensions. Source (Science or the Scientist) has provided us with an amazing and well-rounded vehicle for navigating as humans.

Our reproductive bodies are made up of sex hormones, or chemicals—passionate fuel systems that drive us to produce children and/or a lifetime of important and creative projects. We attract mates or groups of people to follow us and support our endeavors.

Sacred Ocean

Because the womb is the human source of creation, or the gateway, the vessel from which all human life flows, deemed and assigned so by the *Source* of *all* creation, it is vital that we take a good hard look at this rhythmic design to take advantage of its potential for maximum female health and happiness. Our rhythm is our instruction guide to being a woman. When we understand our energy cycle, we stay healthy. When we understand how our bodies function sexually and in conjunction with our rhythm, we can experience ongoing pleasure and satisfaction with our partners. When we understand our mental rejuvenation cycle, we stand in our power. When the female feels good about life, the circles around her feel the positive effects.

As co-creators, men plant their seed, but the merging happens inside of the woman—*her* body accepts or rejects. When in utero, we learn how to have a pulse on what it is to love, how to bond with others, and what it is to trust. All humans develop, swim, and sleep in the rhythmic ocean of the sacred female womb before taking their first breath of Earth's air. All humans are trained for nine months (or thereabouts) to sway to the heartbeats of their mothers and to live solely from their bodies (perhaps this is our first lesson on how to live in harmony with our natural resources as humans on Mother Earth).

A mother, whether she knows it or not, imparts her rhythm of strength, soul, emotion, humility, and "survival wits" onto her developing child. This is Human Sacred Geometry, the relationship of the part to the whole. It is a serious and sacred undertaking. The ideal "pure" human race has nothing to do with the color of the skin or cultural bloodline—it is a people who are whole in mind and spirit from the beginning. Achieving this can only begin to happen when each and every mother has the *willingness* to consciously impart love, nurturance, and feelings of safety to each and every developing fetus, with joy. If children do not pass through the gateway with this important imprinting, a disadvantage is created from the beginning of his or her personal life journey. The child and the culture it is born into suffer the consequences.

Leading a Nation or Leading a Herd of Children— It's All the Same

This same Human Sacred Geometry model applies to the creation of anything—any project or any business. Focus, dedication, and love must set the precedent from the start in order for it to survive and succeed. Because women are hard-wired with this blueprint for a successful beginning, it is crucial that we balance our planetary think tanks *not* with the ways that women have learned from men, but with the deep and innate knowledge and sacred wisdom of the female *in addition* to the solidity of the male. We can just as easily lead a nation as we can a herd of children, and we are meant to. The left and right hemispheres of our brains give us individual gender balance, but since men and women access them differently, our two-gender species can only create a balanced planetary home when both gender-ways work as a team.

> Did you know that when your grandmother was five months pregnant with your mother, the egg that would eventually become you was already present in your mother's womb? That means, before your mother was even born, your mother, your grandmother, and you all shared the same biological environment. Whatever intense feelings (grief, trauma, etc.) affected your grandmother likely affected your mother and you.
>
> —Mark Wollyn

Whether a woman has children or not, or whether she wants to believe it or not, her vessel's cycle dictates her life rhythm from the time she is a girl, a newborn in fact. It is vital that we support and honor women in order for them to be at the ultimate elevation of security and confidence needed to impart their inner guidance—whether nurturing a baby or advising the world community. We must hold them in high esteem.

The Sacred Feminine Lineage

There are only three kinds of females, no matter which race, religion, culture, or village: those who have not yet bled, those who bleed, and those who bleed no more. These are the largest tribes we live in, made up of sisters we know and do not know, but share an intimacy only we understand. Out of honor, I respectfully call these universal tribes *Pre-Bloods*, *Blood Givers*, and *Blood Keepers*. The names may sound cryptic at first, but they are honest interpretations of our raw female experience and reality. I was awakened one night with these identities, and the following interpretations presented, after seeing Clio Wondrausch's painting called "Blood Keeper."

Pre-Bloods

After having two sons, I gave birth to a daughter. I marveled at how different her tiny body was from that of my boys. Her hips were so high and pronounced—everything about her seemed different.

If I remember correctly, it was only an hour or two after she was born when I noticed fluid dripping from her nipples and yoni. Whoa! I asked the midwife what *that* was and she said, "Oh, that's *your* estrogen coursing through her body." I remember saying, "Wow, we are leaky vessels from the time we are born." I never saw that with my boys, although apparently it can happen with males, too. In addition, as a mother's estrogen travels through her newborn girl's uterus for a few days before exiting, a mini-period can be activated.

Mother-to-daughter, we jump-start our girls' life-long rhythms with this brief visitation from the Divine, swiping an imprint that will set into motion the pulse that will become her own unique blueprint of wisdom, anointing her into the lineage of the Sacred Feminine.

While enjoying the freedom of hard play and innocence, our little girl bodies run on the evolutionary path of inevitability. Unknowingly prepping our rhythmic bodies, we begin by first developing our mental and physical energetic recycling patterns. Learning to swim in these waters early on establishes a strength and awareness that will be needed to surf the larger waves of the hormonal rhythm when it arrives.

Truthfully, little girls are often fascinating to be around. Wise beyond their years, astute and often nurturing from the get-go, a well-rounded yet immature view emerges. Sureness or struggle regarding identity, gossiping about others, and battles over leadership are signs that, below the surface of the personality and skin, this rapid growth is firing off quickly and in all directions. When we don't know what it is, getting a grip on it might not ever happen—management always seems to be slightly out of reach. This undetected, frantic,

earthly pulsating rhythm is building, molding, prodding, and pushing as it tries to find its way to calm clarity and authenticity; a caterpillar in its cocoon is working its transformative magic.

I noticed that, as my daughter was reaching the completion of this first phase of her life journey, the volcanic rumblings of her inner core began to take over. The closer the lava got to the surface, the warmer her body actually got. I witnessed what I believe was a series of hot flashes. I am now convinced that we get them at the coming and going of menses.

It is vital that, as adult males and females, we help our *Pre-Bloods* navigate their world to get comfortable in their own skin. We must help every girl to acknowledge the rhythmic undulations of her mental and energetic recycling systems, recognize her gifts, and build on her skills so that she will have a strong foundation in place when womanhood, the *Blood-Giver*, arrives at her doorstep.

Blood Givers

Our teenage years jolt us into the reality of surfing with the big girls, and we learn to develop our sea legs quickly or get crushed by the onslaught of waves. We learn to live our lives while also managing our bodies. There's no turning back.

The entire purpose of the reproductive recycling system is to create, produce; to give life to anything and everything we are a part of. Whether we are mothers of children and/or mothers of invention, our rhythmic cycles have us building relationship circles, big or tiny, wherever we go. We are connectors. We are compassionate care-givers and big-picture motivators.

Most women I know are giving and doing from the time they wake up in the morning until the time they lie their heads down on their pillows. Then they continue to participate into the dark hours of the night, keeping their men satisfied and satiated, or attending to a child who can't sleep. We feed from our breasts and we give from our hearts. We work hard to stay healthy, beautiful, and centered for our own self-esteem and to attract the people we want to have in our lives, personally and in business. We constantly feel pulled at because someone always needs *something*, and the truth is, we give it to them (sometimes with directions), because this is the way we hold our circles together. Giving, producing, and directing is the medicine we provide. It brings us joy and satisfaction to do so unless we allow it to drain us. Mother Nature knows it requires super strength, so we are handed the blueprint of our feminine cycle to give us instruction and guidance on exactly how to achieve this when our bodies are build-ing and then purging in the form of blood every month. This is where 4s4w comes in, to help reveal this blueprint for resting, building, man-ifesting, and problem-solving. Here we learn to give ourselves permis-sion to honor ourselves, which in turn allows us to honor others in the right way. The sequence of each rhythm is a magnificent and inge-nious working machine, the caring engine that runs our communities and therefore societies, the bonding glue that holds it all together.

As if this isn't enough during our Blood Giving years, many of us become warriors who enter the realm of pregnancy and childbirth, a solo journey into the unknown because each experience is unique. Our bodies, minds, and spirits are tested no matter how many times it is done, facing many joys and hardships along the way. It is often a frightening experience, testing our resilience, self-esteem, humility, body image, and coping skills. We can experience great loneliness.

When our gestated child decides it is time to make the grand entrance, we face the fight of our lives. With better medical care today, we do not see the one-in-eight maternal deaths of our 1600s ancestors, but these numbers should be a reminder that delivering a child is not for the wimpy.[12] Childbearing is the most intense female rite-of-passage, the situation that forces us to grow up and get tough right now or, possibly, die. While it is true that some women experience minor discomfort in the process and it is true that our brains provide a mechanism for forgetting the experience after the fact, the truth of the matter is that childbirth is often torture that one must endure, breathe through, and manage for a short or very long amount of time. My immediate thought and feeling after my first child was born was how amazing we women are, that no one would ever be able to convince me that we are weak. I now knew the secret of exactly how powerful we are: *beyond measure.*

Exhausted, we must go on to deliver the placenta, endure more contractions while the uterus goes back to normal size, and work our way through painful nursing of our baby until our nipples toughen up, as well as deal with bleeding for another six weeks to shed the remains of our infant's former habitat.

I have done it three times and had three different experiences. Two of my three births moved along smoothly. Even so, I am not going to tell you that birds were singing and bells were ringing. My third birth was tough. At one point it was everything I could do to hang on to my sanity. It was the most pain I could ever imagine living through. Childbirth is raw. It is tribal. It is spiritual. It is the cosmic rhythms coming together at the moment of truth. It is creation, facing death, all at the same time, a force of Nature like no other, the explosive coming together of Nature and Spirit.

I am proud of making it through the test of a lifetime. I feel honored for the privilege of *giving* birth to three souls. To this day, when I see my grown kids, I know that *gratefulness* lives deep inside of me—that no matter how the Universe works, I feel they chose me to be their mother. The pregnancy and childbirth experience stretches both our skin and our resolve. We wear, on our bodies and within our deepest essence, the scars of our tears and the marks of our ceremony for the rest of our lives, the only true badges of honor we will ever receive as ours alone for the sacrifice.

We are one and the same with the Yucatan village women who are recognized and respected for shedding the highest form of blood, *creation blood*, for their people. We too *give* creation blood every month as a sacrificial tithing to the birthing and well-being of our communities and our planet.

Blood Keepers: Harnessing the Power Within

Menopause is the time when we've stopped giving our blood away every month for population purposes in exchange for keeping and nurturing the power within us. Transitioning from a rhythmic *recycling* system to a rhythmic *recirculating* system, we begin to use our powerful blood to fuel and expand the wisdom of our infinite cores. Menopause can happen naturally in our 40s, 50s, or 60s, or it can be initiated through hysterectomy at any age. At this point we discover that there is a responsibility in not giving it all away anymore. We become Blood Keepers.

As Pre-Bloods, our female bodies begin the pulse that will eventually develop into a unique rhythm within a prescribed sequence, a little like a fingerprint. This rhythm comes to fruition in tandem with our sisters during our Blood-Giving *creation* years, teaching us how to be healthy, well-rounded individuals mentally, physically, emotionally, and spiritually. We learn to identify and manage our many cycles within this rhythm, including a mental rejuvenation cycle, a physical energy cycle, and a sexual cycle. The 4s4w symbolism serves as the instruction manual for surfing this rhythmic sequence.

By the time we are Blood Keepers, most of us are done raising small children and perhaps are in the process of figuring out our next career. One thing is for sure: we've lived and learned. After naturally living our creation rhythm for over 40 years of our lives (and longer if we are on rhythmic hormone replacement), we continue to carry the gift of this rhythm within us, gathering our gifts of knowledge, experience, and heart. The hormones of our ovaries may cease to produce, but our energetic bodies are alive and well and do not forget.

Our bodies, wired as females to support this rhythm, continue to ebb and flow on auto-pilot. For instance, when I was a young mother, I would stand and rock my baby while talking with someone, perhaps for hours if I was at a party or family gathering. If someone came and took the baby from me, I would find myself continuing to rock. I found myself rocking a great deal of the time whether I had the baby in my arms or not. By attentively tuning in to or tracking our cyclical monthly rhythm by the phases of the Moon, we can once again see and feel it.

We have paid our dues, surrendered to our body shapes, and are less vulnerable to what others think about what we do or say. We have suffered and endured the hardships that come with being a reproductive woman, which makes us compassionate beings to the suffering of others. We want it to stop and our Wise Woman no longer takes "no" for an answer.

Instead of becoming mothers who raise children, we become mothers who raise the *world*. We oversee, advise, and make sure that the things that need to be addressed are done so. We become connected to all in a big and fearless way, as if we've finally stepped into our big girl shoes. Like the Yucatan *elder* women who step forward with a fully ragged staff, or the International Council of Thirteen In-

You don't become a true medicine woman until you stop bleeding.

—Jaya Opela

digenous Grandmothers who have stepped forward to speak for Mother Earth, our status deserves and demands to be heard.

Ovulation Nation

Spanning in age from birth to 100 years or more, girls and women share an innate knowingness, a secret to the Universe. With Ovulation as the focus and ultimate purpose for our design, our bodies are wired in rhythmic symphony from the time we take our first breath to the time we take our last. We are the Mystery in human form. Living in alignment with our rhythm is the key to our connection to all. No matter what our individual body circumstances are, we are a web of sisters. We are the Ovulation Nation.

In the Raw

Let's talk about SEX. I believe we can all use some reminders and tips for sorting out our libidos, but in *this* chapter I'm going to address the MEN. It's important that I talk about sex before talking about the woman's cycle, because it will provide a deeper understanding of how the cycle actually functions in relation to her sex cycle.

There is a physical explanation as to why, when you do something during sex, it "turns on" your lover, yet when doing the *exact same thing* another time, it doesn't. In other words, you've discovered that she likes having her shoulders kissed, but you try it another day and she moves away. Does this sound familiar? It's not that your touch is no good, or that she's crazy and changes her mind a lot, or that she's unpredictable. It's the opposite: she's *very* predictable once you learn her monthly pattern of responsiveness. Women have a much higher and steadier sex drive all month long than what we've been taught. However, if you expect her to react the same way all the time (in the way that *you* usually do), you're going to be disappointed. Not only that, but you're going to experience a woman who ends up turning you down more often than not, just to be less confusing, or because she *does* begin to identify it as "not good" sex. *No sex is better than having irritating sex and faking it.* Remember, you've got a steady burn like the Sun, but she follows the ebb and flow of the Moon. She needs variety. To women, clear and ongoing communication about what she likes sexually, and working as a cooperative team, are some of the biggest aphrodisiacs of all.

Women's bodies are rhythmic, cycling through a predictable monthly melody, so she is going to respond to sex differently throughout a month's time. The problem here is that, for a great deal of history and throughout most cultures, there has been a failure to accommodate or acknowledge this rhythm. It has been easier to believe that women are simply not understandable, or worse: they're somewhat hysterical, just too emotional, or not sexual at all, especially after having children or going through menopause. *Wrong.*

Until you know her pattern (by learning the 4s4w system), the best thing you can do is tune in to whether she's responding or not. If she's not responding, and especially if she's recoiling, back off! If she's responding to your advances by coming closer, sounding pleased, and/or actively participating, then continue! It really *is* that simple.

The Sacred Geometry of Sex

We can't truly talk about the female reproductive cycle, or sex cycle, without talking about the primal Sacred Geometry of sex. The pattern of how we respond to sex at different times throughout the month corresponds with the more deeply rooted purpose and process of the reproduction journey. Sexual romance, labor and birthing, and nursing a baby are separate but parallel universes which share the same body machinery and paths to ecstasy. We are going to explore the "sameness" of these universes by looking at how the various body parts are used and what they trigger. It is time to get personal, intimate, and physical.

The Jaw and Labor

Birthing a baby is as raw as we women get. When having a baby, labor contractions prime and squeeze the uterus to assist the child to slowly drop further into the birthing canal to be pushed out. These contractions hurt like hell, which causes the body to tighten. Our natural reaction is to do our best to escape them, yet it's futile. The more we fight the contractions, the worse the childbirth experience is.

When I was in labor with my first child, my midwife told me to *relax my jaw*, explaining that when the jaw relaxes, the uterus relaxes, followed by the rest of the body. When in labor, the objective is to get the uterus to flex and release easily, allowing the opening, or the cervix, to expand enough for the baby to pass through in a fairly efficient manner without obstruction or unnecessary delay. I soon figured out that if I focused solely on relaxing my jaw during the super-strong contractions that muscle relaxation *would* indeed happen, rippling out through the rest of my body in the form of an epic shock wave, but with good results in making progress. Learning to "blow" during labor is the same concept—it relaxes the jaw. Try it without letting your teeth bite down. It's sort of impossible to clench your jaw while blowing out.

Skipping this important "trigger" *could* set off a different result. In this case, if no action is taken to relax the uterus, labor could take many hours more, perhaps even causing the cervix to swell and close. There is no guarantee that it will work, but being attentive to what the jaw is doing during labor is a really great example of how one action can lead to one result, while doing another, or taking *no* action, might lead to another result. These same triggers and results mimic themselves during *sex*.

The Jaw and Kissing

We can apply the primal purpose for the jaw when delivering a baby to understanding the primal purpose of the jaw during intimacy.

Just as the jaw relaxes the uterus during labor, *kissing* is an act that relaxes the jaw, which in turn relaxes the uterus (as long as the kissing is enjoyable), which in turn begins to warm the whole body and sexual organs in preparation for more (if both people decide to go there). We begin to *melt*.

The Skin

When a woman is in labor and in the middle of the shockwave of a contraction, all nerves are electrified and the skin is sensitive to the touch. The body is purging and is pushing its contents out in the form of yelling, sweating, and pushing the baby down. Nerves are on edge.

I instructed everyone attending the birth of my last child not to touch me unless I asked to have my shoulders or back massaged. When something is trying to work its way out of the body, sensations coming *in* often feel highly irritating.

The Skin and Romance

The same thing happens for a woman when romantic touching is going on. The same exact touching technique may feel incredibly good one day and another time feel quite annoying. That's because a woman's body goes through building energy and purging energy throughout a month's time. If she's building, she is accepting compliments, massages, and sensuous touch. If she's purging, her body is recycling physical and emotional junk that is no longer needed. As she pushes these toxins out, she might not want excessive stimulation coming in. Check in with her.

The Nipples-Uterus Connection

During labor and delivery, just as the jaw *relaxes* the uterus and the rest of the body, stimulating the nipples *stimulates and tightens* the uterus and causes the veins in the genitals to engorge with blood. This causes a set of glands called the Bartholin glands to release mucus into the vaginal canal to soften, lubricate, and make the opening more elastic.

If contractions are slow to show and need some help moving along, rolling the nipples between the fingers causes the hormone *oxytocin* to be released from the mother's pituitary gland, which will help to kick the contractions into gear. If there continues to be no reaction of contractions, a super-dose of oxytocin, *Pitocin* (a synthetic), is injected into the woman with more radical results. At this point the contractions can come on strongly.

After the baby is born the nipples continue their work. When the baby is put to the breast, it not only serves as nutrition for the baby, but the stimulating and sucking triggers oxytocin once again to "let down" the milk. It also causes the uterus to contract *again*, this time helping it to go back to its normal size, followed by approximately six weeks of bleeding. The sucking causes the uterus to shed everything that's left.

Nipples and After-Contractions

I can't truly talk about the nipples-uterus connection without talking about "after-contractions." After-contractions are the nipples and uterus on steroids, working in conjunction to show a mother exactly *how* well-connected they are, just in case she didn't catch it the first time.

I didn't really notice the after-contractions with my first baby because I was busy trying to get the hang of nursing. I assumed it would be very easy and wonderful, but *everything* hurt and I was exhausted. All I knew was that my body had gone through, and continued to go through, something totally traumatic yet totally natural—a working machine like no other. It was evident to me that it was, in fact, so natural that my body would birth a baby and heal itself with or without me, or it could die trying. My choices were to either learn everything I could to assist it, or fight it all the way and make things much tougher. The one thing I *did* know was that I had just done something completely amazing.

While pregnant with my second child, my Aunt Yvonne warned me that the after-contractions get worse with every birth. She didn't go into any more than that, and I didn't really know what she meant, but I remembered her words when the time came. Once my baby was born and put to the breast, it felt like *intense* labor all over again! I talked to my midwife and she explained that when the baby nurses it causes the uterus to contract and get back to its normal size. It wasn't messing around this time.

Nipples and Nursing

Nursing is an art in and of itself. Some women have no trouble at all. For others, it takes about a month for the nipples to toughen up before it doesn't feel like razor blades are clamping down; for still others, it just doesn't work out for one reason or another. For those who have a baby who is responding, the experience of nursing changes from painful at the nipple *and* uterus to the most erotic sensation imaginable in both those places. This is the intersection where our reproductive, nurturing, and sexual bodies merge as one.

Nipples and Sex

Just as stimulating the nipples releases oxytocin to stimulate or induce uterine contractions during labor, and just as nursing automatically causes the uterus to go back to its normal size, stimulating the nipples during lovemaking automatically releases oxytocin for a sense of trust and well-being, stimulates the uterus, and engorges the clitoral area. Some women swear (and I have to agree) that they have a gigantic V-shaped nerve that goes from nipples to uterus or to the clitoris! This heightened sensation causes the glands to lubricate the vagina, making it elastic and slippery for sexual intercourse. The amount of lubrication and the texture depend on which part of her cycle the woman is in.

Nipples: When and When *Not* to Touch

As you can see, nipples are amazing and wondrous. They are intoxicating little multi-taskers that are both beautiful and smart: (1) They attract a partner by being visually beautiful; (2) they are arousing to play with; (3) they serve as stimulators for the female genital arousal;

(4) they deliver nutrition to a baby; (5) they are comforting to just about anyone who lays their head on them; and (6) they encourage the uterus to contract and return to its non-pregnancy state after childbirth.

Because the uterus and genitals are the body parts ultimately *responding* when the lips, skin, or nipples are stimulated, what is going on below in a woman's uterus during her cycle has an enormous effect on how she will respond to her lips, skin, breasts, or state of mind being engaged. It is important to understand *where* your sweetheart is in her cycle (or in her uterus) in order to know how responsive she will be, assuming all else is good with your relationship.

Week 4, Summer: The week before her Period, the female body prepares to shed and purge the uterine lining. Every nerve in her body becomes heightened as her emotional body begins shedding before her physical body releases in the form of her Period. She is sensitive to stimulation in a negative way. This week corresponds with being in labor. It's as if every nerve is right on the surface, so sounds, smells, touch—all the senses—are hyper-aware. Too much of anything can be irritating.

A woman often knows when she's going to be bleeding soon because her nipples become slightly sore or extremely sore. Just bumping against something or hugging someone too closely can be very painful. As her uterus begins to cramp, readying to purge her uterine nest, she may experience an uncomfortable feeling of fullness and heaviness. During this time, sucking on her nipples can make a woman cramp and bleed (uterine contractions). Conversely, it might *relieve* some of her achiness during this time. Check in—only she knows for sure. There is also a window *just before* her Period when there is a slight spike in her testosterone, causing her to feel extremely frisky and wanting to get in one last jaunt.

Week 1, Fall: This is the week of her Period. Stimulating her nipples might cause her to bleed more heavily. (Remember the way nursing helps to purge the uterus of its lining in the form of blood after childbirth for those six weeks?) Again, check in to know whether she enjoys contact during this time or not. Because sperm can hang out in her body for up to a week waiting for Ovulation, it is vital that contraception be used if no pregnancy is desired.

Week 2, Winter: The week after her Period is the week leading up to Ovulation. Her hormones are rising rapidly and so is her libido, so most likely she'll be affectionate and open to your advances *if* you are getting along well. The nipples might be very tough, hyper-stimulated, and even sticking out a bit, so stimulating them further can make her very, very wet (to help transport the sperm to the egg), which encourages the desire for intercourse. Contraception is a MUST here if no pregnancy is desired.

Week 3, Spring: The first day of this week is Ovulation, the 24-hour period when her egg drops into place to connect with a sperm. This primal act of desired merging creates a desire for merging with you, her partner. Nipples are definitely interested and want to be involved, *if* you're communicating well as a couple. Contraception is a MUST here if no pregnancy is desired.

The days following Ovulation are a little like the days after throwing a huge party. A little rest is needed and a lot of evaluation is going on. Communication is the key here to keeping the love light burning easily.

Any Time in the Cycle: Touching, licking, or sucking on nipples when lovemaking can be a double-edged sword, so it's best to keep the closeness between you alive. The nipples have to be ready or prepared—diving right in may cause the woman to recoil and tighten up even during her most sexual time. Because they are a trigger for lubricating and preparing the woman's body for intercourse, they are a crucial part of foreplay, along with kissing and sensual touch. Start with kissing, stimulating her skin, or alleviating her stress with massage.

Ovulation

We women are intricate and intimate production machines, with our entire feminine cycle assembly line of sexual hormones designed to support ONE event on ONE day of the month: *Ovulation.* Ovulation is the Beauty Queen of our cycle and the reason for all of this fuss to begin with! Ovulation is the Belle of the Ball. She is the President of every nation. She is Miss Universe and all the Disney Princesses put together. She is Mother Mary, Mother Nature, and the Mother of Invention. She is abundance and plenty. She is Oprah. She is CleOpatra. She is the most stunning woman in the world, the smartest, the most powerful, the most productive, the most deserving, the richest, the kindest, the cleverest, the most connected, and the most free. Ovulation is the Divine Feminine: the co-mingling of earthly need and spiritual enlightenment. This is the place where we can check to see if our Authentic Female is shining brightly or covered in layers of dense fog.

Ovulation is the approximately 24-hour period halfway through the cycle when one "ready" egg drops from an ovary into a fallopian tube, where hundreds of sperm could be waiting in order to merge with our gorgeous Queen and our family, our DNA, our ancestors, both male and female.

Being the source of human creation requires a woman to become nothing less than a magnetic sex goddess during the second phase of her cycle. The primal act of attracting the future father of her children shows the world who rules, in the same way that the Full Moon phase of the lunar cycle shows who rules the heavens when it is happening. It causes us to stop and revere it—we can't take our eyes off of it. Both women and the Full Moon become brilliant, sexy, and sacred all at the same time. We are shining, glowing examples of light and love, reflecting back to society the possibilities of humankind.

All this attracting takes maximum energy and preparation and therefore we need our beauty sleep. Like the New Moon phase, our reproductive (or sex) cycle accommodates this need by slowing us down to regenerate while we are bleeding during the first week of our cycle. Every week of the feminine cycle is unique and carries numerous suggestions for expressing or contemplating our joys or pains.

Orgasm

Orgasm is the climax of all of this sexual and mental stimulation. How easily a woman orgasms, as well as how intense it will be, generally follows the same degree of intensity as the foreplay has been and where she is in her cycle. As a rule of thumb, it is going to be more intense as her hormones build and less intense as they decline. Sometimes they will not appear; other times they will take the long and winding road. Depending on the woman and the place in her cycle, they can also happen quickly and furiously.

Inside and Outside of the Bedroom

Foreplay, for the woman, is ongoing and begins *outside* of the bedroom. If you are communicating well, following through on agreements made, and enjoying each other's company, the woman maintains a steady state of satisfaction and pleasure—turned on to being affectionate and connected to the relationship throughout all phases of her cycle. If the woman has to continually remind her man about agreements made, and these agreements are not followed through on, this turns her off in a hurry. Depending on where she is in her cycle, this may manifest in the form of disappointment, frustration, or anger.

Most women I know do not separate the relationship that happens outside of the bedroom with the relationship that happens inside of the bedroom. The man must continually court her.

The Sexual Order

Sensual touch, such as holding hands, arms around each other, or non-threatening massaging or stroking, is a vital form of connection and checking out how the other person is feeling toward you. If the woman recoils here, kissing or going further is not going to improve the situation. If she warms to the touch, kissing would be the next step, as the jaw relaxes and melts the body. Closing the eyes creates saliva while other juices begin to flow.

Nipples and genitals, primarily the clitoris, are sensitive triggers that need to be respected, rather than handled casually. *They* call the shots. They only respond well when they are ready to respond and when they are treated well. If they are the first things touched before warming up the body, no matter where she is at in her cycle, the woman will most likely back away or even get angry.

The Reason for Foreplay

Touching will either relax a woman or cause her to recoil. If she relaxes, then kissing will further her enjoyment by warming and softening her body, as well as relaxing her uterus. Approaching and stimulating her nipples in the way that is most pleasing to her will cause her uterus to contract and release, engorge the clitoris, and cause the glands and blood vessels to lubricate the vagina. The pathway from nipple stimulation to genital arousal is so strong for some women that this action alone will cause orgasm.

Lubrication, pleasant sensations, and relaxation are vital components to sexual satisfaction for women. Without this *foreplay*, women can come out of the sexual encounter feeling dissatisfied at best, bored or annoyed, and even physically scraped or torn in the genital area because of lack of proper lubrication.

How quickly or slowly the foreplay needs to last totally depends on where she is at in her cycle, how well you are getting along as a couple, how she is physically feeling, how overwhelmed she is in life, and whether or not her past sexual experience (with you or others) has been good.

How great your sexual relationship is will depend on how well you both adhere to her rhythmic libido. By following the 4s4w structure, none of this has to be guesswork or confusing. Rather, it can be an arousing adventure.

The Female Rhythm

4. Intro to the Four Weekly Seasons

Relief is in the Rhythm.
—T.S. Wiley

Understanding the Four Weekly Seasons of the Feminine Cycle

To be clear, each season represents one of four phases in a woman's *monthly* cycle. For starters, I'll mark each phase as one week long, with seven days each. As soon as you have a pretty good handle on *your* cycle by tracking it, you'll need to make your personal adjustments by adding days to one week (or phase) and subtracting from others. Your own rhythm will most likely end up with uneven phases. Remember, this is a non-technical guide—it's a symbolic journey of what most of us *experience*—what we can relate to personally. I describe each week by pointing out what is *basically* happening with the hormones, and how they affect our energy, libido, weight, sleep, food, exercise, and mental cycles. This is *not* a scientifically proven method of understanding your cycle, because each woman's *experience* is different. Remember, what you'll be tracking is just that—*your experience*. Once you are in alignment with the pattern of your personal experience, you'll be better equipped to make health decisions with your health practitioner.

As I've mentioned earlier, the system begins with the first day of your Period, because this is how the medical world tracks your cycle, and it's the easiest signpost for you to identify. I call it a "marker" day.

The second marker day is Ovulation, but this is not as simple to identify and can be a moving target, commonly ranging from Day 11 to Day 21. Recent opinions and studies continue to show new results on this, according to Christine Hitchcock, PhD research associate at the Centre for Menstrual Cycle and Ovulation Research (CeMCOR), University of British Columbia, Vancouver. So it will be up to you to learn your own Ovulation tendencies and rhythm. Using an Ovulation kit, which can be purchased online, is going to be much more accurate than trying to guess.

> I've noticed that I shop during the first half of my cycle and then give it all away during the second half.
>
> —Torre Forrest

The best way to help researchers understand this female recycling phenomenon is for more women to track their cycles and report their findings to their health providers.

A Word about Cycles

Amateur astronomer Jessica Vineyard, aka Ms Galaxy (*www.astronomyforeveryone.com*) pointed out to me that, technically, a cycle has no beginning and no end. Because of this, let me explain the 4s4w system: when comparing the Moon and Sun cycles with the feminine cycle, I acknowledge a starting point in all of them in order to align their phases properly. Each of these cycles has a building, manifestation, deconstruction, and rebooting stage. I loosely align the Sun seasons, Moon phases, and feminine cycle at their dark phases.

I really like the analogy of a woman's cycle with the four seasons. Wonderful and enlightening.

—Richard Shepard

Recognizing the Seasons

I identify the weekly seasons with the characteristics of a *progression of months* and what is happening with light, more than anything. The first and foremost thing to remember is that we are *comparing* our monthly cycle to the *characteristics* of yearly seasons.

The 4s4w weekly seasons compare to these months:

Week 1, Fall: October, November, December

Week 2, Winter: January, February, March

Week 3, Spring: April, May, June

Week 4, Summer: July, August, September

The light of the Sun speaks loud and clear. If we identify the rebooting, building, manifesting, and declining stages of the *light hours* of the Sun, we can easily see how they line up with the Moon and female hormone stages.

- We *enter* the dark phase of our yearly

Sun cycle at the Autumnal Equinox, when shorter days and longer nights take over. It's as if someone has flipped the light switch to "off" at 6 PM and we find ourselves getting sleepy much earlier than usual. It's dark outside! The light during Fall is going deeper into its darkness, until it reaches the Winter Solstice. Fall is about darkness, the time to end one cycle and begin a new one—rebooting. This resting, seasonal phase compares to the resting New Moon and the first week of our feminine cycle, the time when our hormones are at their lowest and the phase when we need to be resting and rebooting.

- The Winter Solstice may be the shortest day of the year, but the onset marks a farewell to that same darkness and begins its ascension into the lighter, longer days. When we celebrate the Solstice, we are celebrating the light; we are celebrating the shedding of our darkness to *become* the light. The entire season of Winter is spent *building* light by day. In this same way, this building, seasonal phase compares to the building, Waxing Moon, and the building, second week of our cycle when our hormones are building rapidly.

- By the time Winter has reached the Vernal Equinox, the light is ready to commit to overpowering and working longer hours than the nighttime dark. Spring is about light and more light. In this same way, this fully expressing, seasonal phase compares to the Full Moon in its full glory, and our fully expressing third week and pinnacle of our feminine cycle, Ovulation.

- The Summer Solstice may mark the longest, lightest day, but its position denotes the onset of losing light. Each day of Summer gets shorter and shorter, while the nights get longer and longer, until our days and nights are equal in duration at the Autumnal Equinox, and then overtaken by the dark again. Summer is about declining light. In this same way, this declining, seasonal phase compares to the declining, Waning Moon, and the fourth week of the feminine cycle, when our hormones are tanking and dismantling our uterine nest, preparing to go inward.

4s4w
Comparing and Aligning the Moon, the Sun, and the Feminine Cycle Phases

	Dark/Internal	Ascending	Ovulation	Light/External	Descending
Sun	Fall	Winter		Spring	Summer
Moon	New Moon	Waxing Moon		Full Moon	Waning Moon
Female	Week 1	Week 2		Week 3	Week 4
	2 4 6	8 10 12 14		16 18 20 22	24 26 28

ABonsall

Recap of Sunlight Characteristics:

Fall, Autumnal Equinox–Winter Solstice: Going into the dark

Winter, Winter Solstice–Vernal Equinox: Coming out of the dark, into the light

Spring, Vernal Equinox–Summer Solstice: Light and more light

Summer, Summer Solstice–Autumnal Equinox: Leaving the light, heading toward the dark

COMPARISONS

We'll dive deeply into the experience and symbolism when we get to each weekly season chapter of the 4s4w system, but for now, let's look at the basics:

Week 1: Fall

Week 2: Winter

Week 3: Spring

Week 4: Summer

MONTHS/TIME OF YEAR WITH WHICH TO IDENTIFY THE WEEKLY SEASONS:

Week 1, Fall: October, November, December

Week 2, Winter: January, February, March

Week 3, Spring: April, May, June

Week 4, Summer: July, August, September

USING KNOWN TERMS, THE CYCLE LOOKS LIKE THIS:

Week 1, Fall: The Period

Week 2, Winter: The Venus Week®

Week 3, Spring: Ovulation

Week 4, Summer: PMS (changing this to The Fire Walk)

COMPARED TO THE MOON PHASES, THE CYCLE LOOKS LIKE THIS:

Week 1, Fall: New Moon

Week 2, Winter: Waxing Second Quarter Moon (gaining light)

Week 3, Spring: Full Moon

Week 4, Summer: Waning Fourth Quarter Moon (losing light)

COMPARED TO THE SOLSTICES AND EQUINOXES:

Week 1, Fall: Just past Autumnal Equinox (dark, internal) to just past Winter Solstice

Week 2, Winter: Just past Winter Solstice (building) to just past Vernal Equinox

Week 3, Spring: Just past Vernal Equinox (light, external) to just past Summer Solstice

Week 4, Summer: Just past Summer Solstice (deconstructing) to just past Autumnal Equinox

SYMBOLICALLY, THE CYCLE LOOKS LIKE THIS:

Week 1, Fall: Like falling leaves, shedding what is no longer needed

Week 2, Winter: Building energy rapidly; attracting a partner; sparkling like a glistening mountain; bold; powerful

Week 3, Spring: *Full* expression of self; magnetic; wet

Week 4, Summer: Irritated, as if coping with the hottest day of Summer; preparing to shed physically by shedding emotions

HORMONALLY, THE CYCLE LOOKS LIKE THIS:

Week 1, Fall: Bleeding; resting hormone levels

Week 2, Winter: Estrogen rising rapidly; uterine wall thickening

Week 3, Spring: Ovulation; progesterone begins to rise to support uterine nest

Week 4, Summer: Uterine nest is not needed and gets dismantled; hormones tank

SEXUALLY, THE CYCLE LOOKS LIKE THIS:

Week 1, Fall: *Need* to rest; sweetly connected

Week 2, Winter: Libido rising quickly; sexual; flirty, connected

Week 3, Spring: Most primal and spiritual; sacred sexuality

Week 4, Summer: On edge, but sex can be a release

ENERGETICALLY, THE CYCLE LOOKS LIKE THIS:

Week 1, Fall: *Vitally important* to rest; meditative, visionary, and artistic energy

Week 2, Winter: Electrified; very motivated and active

Week 3, Spring: High is reached with confidence and wisdom

Week 4, Summer: Physical energy high; mental energy focused

First Nature

Because our particular hormones (and therefore our monthly cycles) are what make us female (and are a constant presence in our lives), it is imperative that each and every girl and woman become an expert on her own rhythm. It is important to know how to track and read your cycle to the point that it becomes second nature because, after all, it's really *first nature*. It is basic Nature. It is your root language, and you need to learn it in order to understand as many aspects of your health as you can. It is also a survival skill for women in general. The more women we have tracking and understanding their cycles, the more health providers, nutritionists, and exercise trainers will incorporate the information into their consulting. More importantly, scientists will have more data for women's health research.

Let your womb be your compass.

—Jaya Opela

Your Unique Rhythm

I use the words "you" or "your cycle" throughout the explanations of the seasonal weeks because it is easier to write and teach you if I am talking to and referring to *you*. I want to share what I know about the characteristics of the weeks—just know that you are unique and you will need to adjust the things that I suggest that do not resonate with you and discover what does. Ultimately you'll need to find your own rhythm.

Hormonal Landscape

Hormonal changes are scientifically proven and verified by experts, yet the exact details of hormones still vary from woman to woman and are affected by that woman's health and well-being. I'm giving you the basics of the natural rhythm *without* alteration from taking birth control pills or hormones, from having a hysterectomy, or from going through menopause, just so that you are aware of what the feminine cycle does in its purest form (though these altered rhythms are briefly addressed). From there, you will need to adjust according to your situation. This will give you a good base of knowledge for discussing your health with your practitioner.

These weekly, seven-day seasons are part of a cycle—part of a rhythmic circle so there is a constant "arch" going on. No one day is identical to another in its purpose or hormonal makeup. Just like the seasons in a year, your feminine cycle is always participating in moving from one weather change to another—in this case, building energy, losing energy, and then starting all over again. The bottom line is that, as a woman, you are constructing a warm uterine nest in which to incubate a baby should a pregnancy occur and deconstructing the nest if one does not, every single month.

4s4w and Birth Control

Since we're talking about a woman's natural rhythm, which in its most primal form is designed to support reproduction (but hosts many cycles in one—sex, beauty, mood, physical energy, communication, evaluating), it is important that we take a moment to briefly go over birth control.

I also want to note here that if you are in perimenopause, the time in life when your natural rhythm begins to change (generally in your 40s), it is imperative to use contraception all month long. For more information about this phase, please read about perimenopause in Chapter 9.

I want to be clear that I am 100 percent in favor of using reliable contraception when no pregnancy is desired. Vasectomy, female sterilization, intrauterine device (IUD), and implant are the most effective methods because the woman does not need to do anything to maintain it once the procedure is secured.

Abstinence is a behavior and is completely effective only if one truly understands the dedication and discipline required to stick with it with absolutely no slip-ups. It also requires an understanding that semen cannot go near the vaginal opening, because those swimmers could make their way inside. In addition, one must be taught the skills to communicate effectively with one's partner, and be strong enough to say no if, or when, intimacy begins to get out of control. Abstinence requires a great deal of education, maturity, and strong self-esteem to be successful.

Other forms of contraception choices, such as The Pill, birth control shot, patch, condom, sponge, ring, etc., vary in effectiveness based on the method and how easy it is to use correctly. For instance, The Pill is extremely effective if it is taken at the same time every day. If one begins to miss doses, it becomes less effective. Research various methods online and speak with your health practitioner to determine the best choice for you.

Even though the 4s4w concept is based on the natural monthly hormonal rhythms of women, this strategy in no way promotes the Rhythm Method of birth control, which is based on your past cycles and assumes that your cycle will continue to be the same. It is therefore only 50 to 60 percent effective. For those who are interested in learning and practicing natural birth control, I highly recommend that you explore the Fertility Awareness-Based Methods (FAM), which track what is happening with you now. They are more detailed, and therefore much more effective, than the Rhythm Method. However, like abstinence, this requires diligence. You must also refrain from having intercourse during the days that your libido wants it the most, or be willing to use another type of contraception during that time.

The most important thing to understand about any form of The Pill (implant, shot, patch, etc.) is that it prevents Ovulation, so it keeps your naturally rhythmic libido from reaching the high it would normally reach. Yet these forms of birth control are highly effective when used correctly. Because of this, your sex drive could actually reach the same high simply from knowing that you need not worry about pregnancy. Being on The Pill is very freeing this way, and this freedom may turn out to be an aphrodisiac for you. I hope to see birth control developed that is effective and healthier for us, and as close to our natural rhythms as possible.

The best form of birth control is knowledge. The 4s4w system gives you a base to launch from in order to make the best decisions possible for yourself regarding food, sleep, exercise, sex, relationships, and birth control. It is my hope that you'll discover a confidence you didn't know you had by getting in touch with the power that fuels your feminine core. It is important to understand how your natural rhythm works in order to make the most intelligent choices for your unique body, mind, and heart.

If you are resistant to exploring the feminine cycle, or if you are somewhat rigid in your view on how it works, then you might balk at the suggestions I'm making. You might even think this book looks like a horoscope version of the menses!

No matter what your religious or world views are, I'm asking you to consider the multidimensional facets of your biological body and its connection to all layers of the biological rhythms of our Universe. The feminine cycle is a raw, basic function, yet incredibly and vastly *smart*. It is difficult to know all of what it affects. It is the source that forms the solid roots of our female bodies. From these roots we nurture our own trees of life.

The Psychological Landscape of "Mind Moods"

"I am hoping that you will address the mindful moods of each weekly season. I find that, from week to week, I can have a completely different train of thought. One week I can be very easy-going and the world is not an overwhelming place. The next I can be irritated with the way everything works and think that I have the power to change it. The next: it's a hopeless state we are all living in, nothing can be done, just protect the children. And then the cycle starts all over again."

Barbara, a gal pal of mine and one of my case study volunteers, was able to attach a name to the very thing that was plaguing me: my ever-changing views on things. I wasn't "changing my mind"—I was just seeing things a little differently from week to week—I was viewing the same situation from different angles: "mindful moods," which from here on out I am calling "Mind Moods." By tracking my cycle, I began to understand how these Mind Moods actually make me an extremely well-rounded thinker when I have their pattern mastered.

Once I began to tap into my natural rhythm I began to see what was going on. I realized that I actually morph through different archetypes: Lounging Queen, Visionary, Artist, Builder, Fun Date, Lover, Goddess, World Leader, Athlete, Fire Walker, and Monk, and no, this is not madness! It is an opportunity to naturally express the many beautiful facets of your individual personality and your overall being. There is an absolute rhyme and reason for showing all sides of you. You are presenting your *whole* self throughout the month and, when in tune, you are becoming your Authentic Female Self. As creators of our families and global circles it is vital that we embrace our ability to view an issue from many different angles in order to understand what makes us wise and compassionate leaders.

The psychological and emotional changes I observe as women's experiences are *not* scientifically proven to the extent in which I speak of them. As women, we all know these changes in our perception exist, as Barbara expressed earlier. Many other health practitioners, midwives, and lay people have written very similar takes on the thought-changes I am describing and the symbolism they represent. The truth is, the more often the feminine cycle sequence is revealed, the easier it is for everyone to see these very logical and predictable patterns.

The symbolic interpretations and suggestions I make are also *not* scientifically proven. They are ways to understand how the cycle performs. They are tools for remembering how to navigate your experience and relationship to your cycle. In no way should this system be taken as medical advice. It should be used and viewed as a *support* tool for discussing and receiving advice from your medical practitioner and for your own knowledge of yourself.

Use my descriptions and explanations as a *template only*. Take note if you experience the same things as I describe. Take note if you don't. Then ask yourself what you *do* experience. Do you have a predictable pattern that you can begin to utilize for your health and well-being? Write it down. The best way to begin to tap into YOU is to question what I'm suggesting. If you do so, you will become more *attentive* to the nuances of what you actually feel and experience.

Reading 4s4w

The descriptions of each season and each Moon phase are *characteristics only*. These *characteristics* compare to the characteristics of each feminine cycle week. Remember, the "season" or Moon phase I'm talking about represents one of the weeks in the monthly cycle. For instance, when I'm talking about Winter, I'm talking about Week 2 of the cycle and how it *compares* to Winter. You will have a Week 2, Winter, for every single month throughout the year.

As I talked about earlier in this chapter the descriptions of the seasons are as *I* know and experience them and how the general population refers *to the months, or times of year, that they relate to.* You may have an entirely different take on the seasons, depending on where you live. I live in the northern hemisphere, in Oregon, USA. You may live in the southern hemisphere, in Australia, where your seasons are opposite from mine. If you cannot relate to the way I describe the seasons, then toss or scramble them and just stick to understanding the other symbolic references and hormonal landscape of the cycle. The only thing that is important is for you to understand your own monthly rhythmic pattern.

The Categories

Each weekly season has its own color-coded chapter for your convenience, with the same sub-headings as the others, describing its unique rhythm. Each week has:

Key Words and Bullet Points: This is an at-a-glance view of the characteristics of each week in the feminine cycle and how they compare to the seasons and the Moon phases.

Overview: A brief description of the same.

Hormones: Easy-to-understand, *basic* biological processes.

Fertility Awareness (if you are not on The Pill): What you need to be aware of if you don't want to get pregnant.

If You are on Some Form of The Pill: Brief comments on how it affects your natural rhythm.

Characteristics of the Feminine Cycle: A description of the feminine cycle *experience* during each particular week.

How the Characteristics of the Season, the Moon and the Feminine Cycle Relate: The premise of the book. Comparing these characteristics helps to remember what is happening each week.

Influences on the Body: The *physical* symbolic transitions and influences of each week; physical symptoms and energy levels.

Influences on the Mind: *Mind Mood* symbolic transitions and influences for each week; how our views and focuses change and what they might represent; how to take advantage of each Mind Mood for an optimal experience.

Challenges: Things to be aware of.

Transitioning from One Week to the Next: A recap of the past week and what to look forward to in the next.

Final Thoughts: Final summary or extra comments.

To-Do List: Suggestions for implementing 4s4w.

Personal Inquiry: Basic questions to be answered every month.

The ManGuide: Information for him.

Combination Health

For me, walking around and working with an approaching migraine nearly 24/7 for years and years finally motivated me to get truly serious about paying attention to what I was putting in my mouth, what time I went to bed, how I exercised, what kind of stress I was under, and what was going on for me hormonally, because I wasn't really sure what the source of the problem was.

I saw doctors—all of them: Western, Homeopathic, Naturopathic, Chinese, Chiropractic, etc. I got massages, reflexology, acupuncture, and physical therapy. I did yoga, meditated, breathed, and worked out at the gym. I didn't eat the foods that supposedly trigger migraines. I went vegetarian, vegan, macrobiotic, carnivore, everything-in-mod-eration, no sugar, no gluten, no caffeine, some caffeine, liver cleanses, and so on. I checked my hormones through blood and saliva tests. I visited websites. I read books. I learned from my author friend, Janis Hunt Johnson, to first ask for guidance-from-above and within to not allow an illness to attach itself to me when I felt the onset of imbal-ance, and eventually as a prevention measure.[13] None of them alone fixed me, but *all* of them continue to help me. It's a matter of knowing what goes where and when. I'm finding the balance because I finally started to understand that my body is rhythmic—it *isn't the same* body every day. I also began discovering that I *do* have power over this rhythm by surfing it and staying on top of it.

I call it *Combination Health* because it reminds me of trying to find the right individual numbers to unlock the combination lock on my bicycle. If one is off, the thing won't open. For me, I know there is not one fix-it-all cure. I have to keep adjusting the numbers (nutri-tion, exercise, sleep and rest, hormones, stress reduction, connection to others and spirit, soul and heart attention) until I get the *right* combination for *me*. Since it changes daily I have learned to become an expert on my natural biological rhythms and personality patterns and habits. Each day has a different lock to decode, but the whole pattern is repeated, for the most part, on a monthly basis. Weather conditions and life circumstances are huge variables, so they also get factored in. Our bodies give us pretty much instant feedback if we choose to pay attention. The key is learning to listen to your body and being attentive to its signals and predictable cues.

The Gift of Rhythm

I've discovered that becoming an expert on my own natural monthly hormonal rhythm has made all the difference in the world with help-ing me to make better choices regarding my other health assessments such as food and sleep, or business and relationship decisions. They are all working together to open the lock to my overall health and well-being. If my nutrition is off, it will affect my sleep and hormones, for instance. If I slack off from exercising, I pay the price with not sleeping well or allowing my circulation to slow down. This initiates a domino effect, causing me to be tired and eventually headachey and stiff, at which point I find myself absent-mindedly drinking coffee to pick me up. This little caffeine trick may actually work for one day, so I'll try to get away without exercising the next day as well. I'll push my luck. I actually love to exercise, but if I have writing to finish, for instance, I'll put off the gym or a hike, thinking I'll get to it later. This is where the downward spiral of poor decisions lands me in a pile of fatigue, headaches, colds, stress, disappointment, cancellations, and apologies.

It takes discipline. It does! It takes being open to new ways of doing things and dropping habits that no longer serve you. It takes being lusciously attentive to taking care of *you* in a well-rounded way. What applied yesterday does not necessarily apply today. It is a constant adjustment throughout our lifetimes. I've learned not to take on anything I don't enjoy. I *enjoy* tracking my cycle and noticing the nuances of *me*. I love it, in fact.

I've learned to get into my combination health: I love eating well, sleeping well, and properly exercising my body, mind, and soul. The way I must begin this process is to start the day by knowing exactly where I am in my rhythmic monthly hormonal cycle and what it means physiologically, psychologically, and symbolically on that particular day.

Mele Ohana

I have learned to appreciate the wisdom and the hard work of the women who came before me:

- The indigenous grandmothers who felt the rhythms of Mother Earth and Father Sky, who appreciated Brother Sun and Sister Moon, and lived in awe of the Great Source

- The brave Suffragists and Feminists who have paved the way for my personal expression to thrive

- The divinity of the female nature—the Sacred Feminine

- My sister-friends who surround me now

- And last but not least, my ongoing discovery of my emerging Authentic Self

I carry all of these inside of me. I am a Sacred Feminist.

I also have enormous gratitude for:

- The men in my life, past and present, who have provided support and security to my unfolding

- The many men of today who desire to live in and are manifesting a world that walks in equal respect with women

- And the men who have asked great questions about this 4s4w concept and who have encouraged me and waited patiently for its publication

I invite you to find your unique rhythm and join me in synchronizing with those of the Universe. Together we can heal our planet with new ideas and move forward from a higher vibration of living.

5. fall

falling leaves
hide the path
so quietly

—John Bailey
Autumn, A Haiku Year

week 1
fall

"Red Leaves Falling"

KNOWN AS: The Period or Menstruation

QUICK VIEW COMPARISONS

- **Week 1 (Days 1–7)**
- **Fall/Winter**
  - **Northern Hemisphere:** October, November, December
  - **Southern Hemisphere:** April, May, June
- **New Moon**

KEY WORDS: Shedding (like leaves falling from trees), Honoring

- **Central Theme:** Letting go and deserved self-indulgence
- **Focus:** It's all about YOU
- **Symbolism:** Shedding things in your life that do not serve you and starting fresh
- **Intention:** Inner peace and honor to self; to release and relax; rejuvenate

FEMININE CYCLE

- **Hormonal Phase:** Menstrual
- **Hormone Activity:** Low progesterone, low estrogen, bleeding

Release ~ Relax ~ Rejuvenate

FALL, THE SEASON (COMPARISON)

- **In Nature:** Leaves shedding/falling from trees; harvesting crops; Autumnal Equinox takes us into darkness with shorter days and longer nights until Winter Solstice marks the least amount of sunlight of the year
- **Foods:** Harvest foods, nurturing sustenance
- **Activity:** Planning for holidays and preparing for Winter

MOON (COMPARISON)

- **Phase to Relate to:** New Moon (Sleeping/Dark/Internal)
- **Moon and Feminine Cycle Phase:** Beginning
- **Moon and Feminine Cycle Days:** 1–7 (adjust feminine cycle days as needed)

CEREMONIAL ENERGIES

- **Four Directions:** West
- **Four Elements:** Earth (roots, reality)
- **Colors:** Deep reds and yellows, brown
- **Chakras:** Root (1), Third Eye (6)

FEMALE BODY

- **Immune System:** Compromised, but starting to build
- **Overall Energy:** Low
- **Physically:** Cramping, water retention
- **Mentally:** Quiet, internal, creative, alert, intuitive
- **Emotional Spectrum:** Relieved, honored, or embarrassed; tired of being a woman
- **Soulfully:** Connected to the collective female; wise, elevated
- **Outward Appearance/Behavior:** Reserved, introverted
- **Senses:** Sight, intuition

Release ~ Relax ~ Rejuvenate

SEX DRIVE

- **Juices:** Sticky, bleeding
- **Nipples:** Tender
- **Orgasms:** Sometimes intense, sometimes absent
- **Ideas:** Gentle touching; spooning; receive feet and shoulder massage; enjoy the affection of just sleeping together

OUTLOOK

- **Overall:** Tends to be humbled with a sense of resignation
- **Archetypes:** QUEEN, VISIONARY, ARTIST
- **Mind Mood Persona:** "I see the potential," creative, hopeful, excited
- **Attitude:** Calm, restricted, or cranky
- **Relationships:** Individual; sweet personal time
- **When Positive:** Feeling relieved, creative, vast vision, centered/connected
- **When Challenged:** Self-loathing, embarrassed, grouchy if not feeling well, overwhelmed, lost, disappointed

SUGGESTIONS FOR YOU

- **Take time** for yourself but no need to block anyone out; enjoy your home
- **Lounge** whenever possible—lay in bed or on the couch with a book
- **Journal** your thoughts about releasing, then jot down new ideas as they come
- **Art:** Paint, do crafts, collages, or organize drawers or files while sitting down

Release ~ Relax ~ Rejuvenate

CARE REGIMEN SUGGESTIONS

- ∿ **Food:** Clean, easy to digest, high protein
- ∿ **Exercise:** Gentle; no upside-down positions
- ∿ **Sleep:** Lots of it—your body is regenerating
- ∿ **Beauty:** Body waxing may be more painful and cause irritation; hair perms might not "take;" wait until the very end of the week or the following week
- ∿ **Clothes:** Pajamas, sweats, lounging attire when at home

SUGGESTIONS FOR HIM

- ∿ **Take over** the bulk of home duties (happily): cooking and kids for the first three days
- ∿ **If no kids at home,** this is the week for that mountain-bike or fishing trip
- ∿ **Keep the energy** of the home mellow and relaxed
- ∿ **Relax as well,** when possible; rent movies for both of you
- ∿ **Be sweet and kind;** massage her feet, fix her dinner; enjoy sleeping together
- ∿ **Elemental Energy:** Free-flowing *water* energy from *you* serves her well by its ability to wrap around and fill in gaps, as well as provide independence for you

Overview
Week 1, Fall

Week 1, Fall starts with the first day of your Period, which is considered Day 1 when tracking your cycle. Factually, you are shedding your uterine lining in the form of bleeding, similar to a tree shedding

Release ~ Relax ~ Rejuvenate

its leaves in autumn. It is really the end *and* the beginning, in the same way the New Moon ends and begins the monthly lunar cycle. Your body is cleansing, basically throwing out the old and preparing for the new. As it does so, you might find your mind filling with visions for the future and your soul embracing hope and well-being. Your hormone levels are "lying low," signaling you to do the same. Relax your mind and let yourself dream.

Mental
Happiness
is Total
Relaxation

—Yogi teabag
saying

Hormones
Week 1, Fall

Your hormones are at their lowest here, allowing a complete cleansing to take place. The uterine lining (or *nest* as I call it) that was so carefully built up in preparation for possible pregnancy disassembles itself and releases in the form of blood (if no pregnancy occurred approximately 14 days earlier). Estrogen begins to rise in order to activate the process all over again.

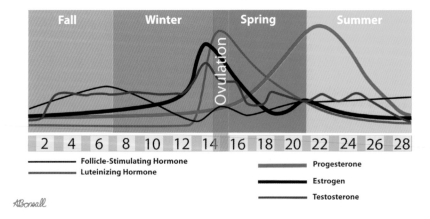

Release ~ Relax ~ Rejuvenate

Your Rhythm and The Pill

Whether you are on The Pill or not, your hormones are lying low this week in order to shed your uterine lining.

Fertility Awareness—If You are *Not* on The Pill:

Since it is possible for sperm to stay alive inside of you for up to seven days,[14] you'll need to use some form of birth control beginning around Day 4 of your cycle, possibly while you're still on your Period if you have sex during this time. Ovulation generally happens around Day 14 or 15, but there are no guarantees on this. I am an early ovulator, which means I ovulate on Day 11 or 12. This very thing caused my pregnancies. I thought I was using contraception (diaphragm, condoms, etc.) correctly and using it in time, but little did I know I waited too long to begin using it. If you don't know when you ovulate, you need to take every precaution until you get a good handle on this. Even then, Ovulation can be mighty inconsistent.

Reproduction Comparison: Birthing Phase

I compare the Period to the Birthing Phase in the reproductive cycle. Since no pregnancy has occurred, we "birth" or shed the unneeded lining of the uterus instead, in the form of blood.

A Blood Benefit: Menstrual Blood Banking

Stem cells are cells that have the ability to duplicate themselves over and over again. They also give rise to every type of cell in the body that cannot normally reproduce themselves well, or at all. When researchers have the ability to produce these new cells, they have more room to discover how to create life-saving treatments for our most horrific diseases such as Alzheimer's and Parkinson's. In this way, stem cells are like a "sourdough starter" (the live catalyst for making sourdough bread) of the human body. Stem cells are in charge of creating new cells to replace old, damaged ones in order to regenerate body parts.

Release ~ Relax ~ Rejuvenate

Stem cells are nothing new—they are part of the amazing human body matrix, waiting for us to see and understand how to use them. All cells in our bodies can be traced back to our small amounts of original stem cells. The Source of the Universe has provided everything we need to sustain abundance and health for plants, animals, humans, and our environment, if only we would pay attention to the science of it all.

Stem cells are retrieved from the earliest stage of eggs fertilized at in-vitro fertilization clinics but did not get implanted in a woman's uterus because they were no longer wanted or needed. They can also be retrieved by syringing the placenta through the umbilical cord after it has been detached from a newborn.

Here's one of the most exciting things of all: a large number of studies show that menstrual blood also contains stem cells.[15] It turns out that the thick growth of blood cells that make up the uterine lining that we shed every month contains regenerative cells. According to stem cell expert Dr. Stephen Noga, director of the Cellular Therapeutics Program at Sinai Hospital of Baltimore, "Even one menstrual cycle has the potential to produce millions of stem cells."[16]

Collection is easy by using a lab kit. A silicone cup is inserted into the vagina on the heaviest flow day for at least three hours and then sent to a Menstrual Blood Bank where it is processed, frozen, and stored for the woman's future use.[17] The downside is that, even though there is no question that menstrual blood contains stem cells, blood banking is expensive and it is not known at this time how usable these frozen stem cells will be in 25 years.

The Push to Take Away the Period

The current trend of ridding ourselves of the Period, interrupting this important part of our female *recycling* system for *casual* reasons or *convenience*, is a practice that discourages me.

There is a push for the four-times-a-year Period or the once-a-year Period through birth control pill manipulation. Chemists are creating it, pharmaceutical companies are distributing it, doctors are

Release ~ Relax ~ Rejuvenate

prescribing it, and women are asking for this rhythm-destroying pill system to relieve them of their feminine cycle ails or scheduling challenges. It *does* most likely provide relief in cases of severe distress—a last ditch effort to gain relief, which otherwise might result in having a hysterectomy, for instance. However, it's an entirely different thing to prescribe it because the feminine cycle is perceived as obsolete or as a curse.

I am in favor of women improving their lives and taking charge to do what they feel is best. Nevertheless, for a society that is already so far out of touch with the natural monthly hormonal rhythm—the blueprint of female intelligence (which has not yet had its due)—my feeling is that this can only lead to alienating us further from what it means to be a strong and healthy female.

Characteristics
Week 1, Fall

Reminder: The 4s4w strategy, or system, was created for the sole purpose of putting the feminine cycle into perspective in order to relate our experiences to its week-to-week and day-to-day changes and remembering how they go without too much effort.

Each woman is different and ultimately must identify and adjust her own rhythm, but the hormonal influences of each phase tend to have the same general characteristics as the seasons. The 4s4w system attempts to add meaning to these characteristics.

The Feminine Cycle (Days 1–7)

In the 4s4w system, I call the first day of your Period, Day 1, a *marker* day. Your doctor will ask, "What was the first day of your last Period?" because it's a reliable point of reference for all aspects of your reproductive body, including possible pregnancy and conception date.

Release ~ Relax ~ Rejuvenate

There is a *lot* of work going on in your body, so the majority of your energy needs to go to *you*, internally. It's time to go inward in pretty much every way. Your physical body needs to relax so that it can rejuvenate properly. Your mind will most likely be very active with great new ideas to explore throughout the upcoming weeks. Once you've given focus to releasing things with love that do not serve you, it's time to be still and allow your mind and heart to expand. I find it to be my most creative week for writing and creating art, as well as my most spiritual week for receiving guidance through prayer and meditation, or just having an open heart and mind.

> Life is a work of art. Sometimes the strokes are broad; sometimes narrow. Sometimes, the work is inspired; sometimes not. In the downtime, we spend time stretching and prepping canvas, so that when the time comes, our lives are prepared for the strokes that come.
>
> —Tzila "Z" Duenzl

How the *Characteristics* of Fall, the Moon, and the Feminine Cycle Relate

Days and Nights: The Autumnal Equinox (the first day of Fall) signals the nights to grow longer than the days (in the Northern Hemisphere) until the Earth reaches the Winter Solstice, when this trend reverses and the days begin to gain light. After the Equinox, it is as though we've been given a sleeping pill in the evenings. The blanket of Fall's early darkness, following the late nights of Summer, always sneaks up on me no matter how many times I've experienced it. Autumn has this darkness in common with the New Moon, as well as this *lying low* phase of the feminine cycle. We need to be resting and sleeping more at this phase of the monthly cycle.

Harvest: Fall is the time of the year when we finish picking any vegetables left on the vine and clear the garden for the dormancy of Winter or a cold weather crop. We cut back overgrown brush from Spring and Summer and rake up the leaves in order to settle into our homes. In this same way, we shed our uterine linings to prepare for a new fertile garden of our own.

Back to School: Unless you or your children attend a year-'round school, going back to school in September is a time of new beginnings in the form of starting from scratch year after year. In this same way, we start from scratch month after month with our feminine cycle. Minds expand during the first school term, organizing, plan-

Release ~ Relax ~ Rejuvenate

ning, and setting oneself up for the rest of the year, as opposed to Spring, when we are busy presenting the projects we've created from these plans. This is the phase in my cycle when I continue to get my best ideas and visions, setting into motion a new cycle of experience for my feminine month and for the future in general.

Creating and Planning: Crafts and creativity come alive in Autumn, more than in any other season, with preparing for the upcoming holidays. While our bodies are lying low during the first week of our cycle, our creativity flourishes with new ideas and artistic expression.

> **Needing more sleep, clearing and preparing the garden,** new beginnings, and artistic expression in Fall are similar to Week 1 of the feminine cycle, which is the best phase for lying low, honoring ourselves, and letting our minds create new seeds of thought.

Symbolic Transitions & Influences
Week 1, Fall

Since **Week 1, Fall** is part of a cycle in motion, the first day of the week is different from the last day of the week. Our physical bodies *and* our Mind Moods change daily.

Influences on the Body: Letting Go and Starting Again

- Weakened
- Low energy
- Cramping
- Need rest and nourishment
- Gaining strength

Release ~ Relax ~ Rejuvenate

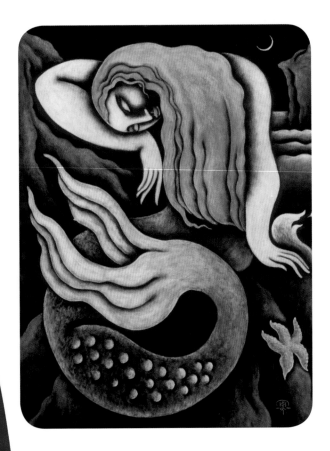

Before I figured out what I *must* do to prepare for this Period week before it starts, I used to pay with built-up water pressure and cramps in my body from inflammation and toxins. I felt as if cement had just been delivered to my pelvis, also causing a headache or dizziness. My sinuses would feel swollen and my nipples tender in an "ouch" sort of way (not a stimulated way). I started to notice a pattern of immune weakness during this bottoming out time, beginning a few days before my Period and lasting until a few days after it started. I discovered that if I get a cold it is usually during this time. This is a good time to watch out for other viruses as well, such as genital herpes or cold sores reappearing, if you get them. It is vital that I don't let myself get run down by literally running around too much, either with exercise, work, or errands. It is easy for exhaustion to sneak up on me in mid-afternoon. If I ignore that signal, I pay the price later. *Overdoing it* by scheduling too many things *is the number one thing* that throws this week out of whack for me in pretty much every way.

During the week *before*, when I follow my own advice in my 4s4w strategy by attending to my eating, sleeping, and exercising, mentally observing and deciding what to let go of, and knowing I am in full *control of* and taking *responsibility for* my life choices, I experience the opposite effect of feeling lousy: I actually experience a euphoric high from releasing all that pressure (in the form of the physical release of blood) and a general sense of serenity, pleasure, and joy. Feeling clear-headed, mentally stimulated, and with my body just heavy

Release ~ Relax ~ Rejuvenate

enough to remind me to keep things mellow, I experience subtle cramps at the most, if any at all.

It's important to note here that your bowels are also doing their best to eliminate what is no longer needed by dumping toxins for a few days before and just after you've started your Period. If you're not feeling a subtle shift in this area, you may be dehydrated. Try drinking water with electrolytes (more sodium) in it, or coconut water (more potassium) to replenish. Pay more attention to this lower trunk area of your body throughout the month, and make sure you're eliminating regularly. I also make sure I take my supplements during the second half of this week to build my system back up. Ask your holistic health practitioner if you need them.

Even though I've found a way to feel good and experience real pleasure from this time in my cycle, I'm not going to sit here and tell you that I've always loved having a Period. It has been humbling and humiliating and bothersome at times, for sure. I think it's really the "mess" aspect that used to get to me. I have never liked to tell my partner that I'm on my Period. Even though he's way cool, it all makes me question my attractiveness. Maybe the whole thing just makes *me* feel unattractive at times. I'm still mortified if I leave even a smidgen of feminine hygiene evidence in eye range of anyone entering the bathroom. Nor have I ever gotten used to buying the stuff at the grocery store without hiding it under the cereal boxes. I try to find a female checker and bag it quickly myself! I'm not sure I'll ever get over this; maybe I don't need to. Certain necessities in my life are simply *personal* and my discomfort is appropriate, reasonable, and just the way it is.

That said, I have to mention and honor the men here. Don't you love a guy who will buy your supplies for you if he is going to the grocery store, they are on your list, and you can't get there yourself? Treat this guy well.

Once the bleeding has subsided, I begin to feel energized quite rapidly and my body springs into action as if I've been held back at a starting gate. I'm ready to implement projects and my libido has been nudging and stirring me to move into my next phase.

Release ~ Relax ~ Rejuvenate

Influences on the Mind and Soul: An Ending *and* a Beginning

Mind Moods and Archetypes

- Honoring
- Releasing
- The Queen
- Visionary and Artist
- Awaken and Emerge

Honoring

In spite of my social discomfort, I've discovered that there are far greater rewards to having a Period than not. I've learned how to honor myself and all the women who came before me during this time. Shedding the uterine lining, like leaves falling from trees to the ground, are Mother Nature's *feng shui* directions for where to focus our attention next. When leaves fall from the tree, our eyes follow them. It's a reminder that, with this shedding, our bodies are grounding us now. Leaves falling from branch to ground point us to look further and deeper into the collective fertile feminine soil of our ancestors and its solid and vast underground root system. We hold the Earth together with our roots by reaching out to find sustenance. We hold hands in our sisterhood for survival and strength. Here we find peace. Misa Hopkins, guardian of a Native Path in the Sacred Feminine, describes it as "shedding our limited bodies to become our limitless selves."

This is the week of the feminine cycle during which our indigenous mothers visited their Moon Lodges to rest and connect with each other. Oral history tells us that, before artificial lighting, women started their Periods on or around the New Moon and cycled together, bleeding on or around the same time.

Even though we were forced by an unenlightened culture to take the secret of our blood life and life blood underground, there is comfort in knowing I am not alone in this womanly journey.

Release ~ Relax ~ Rejuvenate

Releasing

For the first three days or so of my Period I ask everything unhealthy in my body to get flushed out, allowing my healthy cells and tissues to flourish. I visualize conscious cleansing of any emotions that need to go, that I did not take care of in the previous week. I find that tears often follow. I ask myself if there are any habits, activities, or people I need to let go of in order to be in alignment with my values, principles, and my overall health. I sit with this and congratulate myself for taking good care of myself.

THE QUEEN

I've learned to lounge around as much as possible without guilt. I treat myself like the deserving Queen that I am. If *I* don't, how *can* I, or why *should* I, expect anyone else to? I still take care of my responsibilities, but no more than that. I look for opportunities to lie on the couch with a good book (reading or writing it!) and a cup of hot tea.

It's vital that you and your guy get in sync with this. It's important that he takes over dinner for the kids if you're the one who normally does it, for example. He needs to understand the importance of you lying low during this week. If he's not made aware, then he won't understand your need to be a bit lazy and may quickly become frustrated. I don't even exercise during this time if I don't have to. However, I'm not handicapped. This is not a disease! If I'm scheduled to run a half marathon I'll still do it, but I don't push myself beyond what I've committed to. I make sure to lie down on the couch to catch up on my rest afterwards. Take advantage of this time. It's here for a reason. You need to recharge your batteries.

Release ~ Relax ~ Rejuvenate

VISIONARY/ARTIST

Just like the shedding of the uterus, leaves falling from trees show an end to a colorful cycle of seasonal changes. The deep roots they point to represent a sweet and tender beginning that starts from seed and perseveres into a magnificent tree.

During this week, as your Period lightens and you've let go of things no longer necessary, the Visionary in you will step in like a dream, planting seeds of ideas to nurture over the rest of your month, continuing your daily, weekly, monthly, and lifetime cycles without hesitation. Journaling and artwork, expressing your seedlings while you're sitting, with little talking and no television or Internet, using your mind and hands only, adding some music to encourage your Muse, is especially important at this time for rounding out your holistic self. This is soul work, Baby, and you *must* find the time. The Greater Good is talking to you here, or you may simply think of it as collecting and collating your thoughts. You'll begin to marvel at the profusion of ideas you harvest by being still and open to new possibilities. This is meditation in action.

> Your vision will become clear only when you look into your heart. Who looks outside, dreams. Who looks inside, awakens.
>
> —Carl Jung

Release ~ Relax ~ Rejuvenate

You are receiving the bigger picture of what is possible, and it is positive, loving, and uplifting. It is not time to talk but to listen, except for giving prayers of thanks and requests for guidance. I personally take great pleasure in the deliciousness of this luxury. If you can find the time for everything else, you can find the time to do this. You are hereby getting permission and directions to make it a priority! Tell your kids it's "mommy alone-time." Tell your guy, "It is personal time." Tell yourself it's "time for *me*." I love it when my guy sits next to me on the couch reading a book while I'm reading mine. Separate while together is a nice way to do this week.

Alternative: During some months, rather than doing art, I organize. This is a great time to clean out one drawer at a time while hanging out on the couch. Organizing is also an "end and a beginning." You're cleaning out the old, keeping what you want, and arranging it in a way that can help you move forward. I promise you'll feel refreshed and love the results.

Fall is my favorite season and most creative time. Many of my paintings are born at this time of year.

—Mara Friedman Brendt

> **Challenge #1:** If you find yourself stewing and judging others during your quiet time, you have a lot more observing, deciding, and releasing to do in **Week 4, Summer**, next time around. (You'll read about this once you get to the **Week 4, Summer** chapter.) Did you ever see the movie *Groundhog Day* with Bill Murray and Andi McDowell? It's a little like that. Every month you'll get a chance to start over again, to improve upon those things you desire to "get right." For now, it appears you're still releasing and not receiving, so go with it. Keep releasing. Write down the things that are troubling you. It's worked for me to do a collage (cut-out magazine pictures and words glued onto paper) to move that energy along. And then get back on track.

Release ~ Relax ~ Rejuvenate

Note: This doesn't mean that all the things that are bothering you are things that need to, have the power to, or should be gotten rid of. What I'm saying is that it's time to release *the unhealthy* anger (the stuff that keeps you from visualizing good stuff during your quiet time) in order to allow the "highest good" solution to appear instead. In this way you're still addressing a valid concern, causing less harm to yourself, and taking action from a more powerful and productive position. Women can show the way by getting good at this practice.

Womb Wisdom Practice:

1. Acknowledge the negative emotion inside of YOU.

2. Hold and apply love and compassion to this emotion.

3. Visualize the person you are feeling this way about, and recognize him or her as suffering in their own right. Notice compassion.

4. Allow yourself to feel love.

This practice is not about needing something from the other person or excusing bad behavior, nor is it about sending the other person healing vibes. This is about transforming the emotion you are feeling into one that fills *your* body with healing love.

Challenge #2: I've discovered that during this week, especially just before and right after I start my Period, I'm a bit tongue-tied when talking. I'm a speaker and I have times when I just can't spit out what I want to say. I keep stumbling over my words. I began jotting down those episodes and, sure enough, most of the time I was going through **Week 1, Fall**. It's a time to be inward, so it makes sense to me that I literally can't articulate what I want to say as well as I can throughout other weeks. I *am* a better *writer* at this time. It seems the visions in my head flow better through my quiet hands than through my mouth at this phase of my cycle.

Release ~ Relax ~ Rejuvenate

Challenge #3: I'll repeat, the one thing that messes up my rest and my visioning, and potentially the whole month to come, is overdoing it. Remember, this is your recharge time as well as being the portion of the cycle that plants the mental motivational seeds for what's to come. Letting go of things that do not serve you and relaxing your body to stillness in order to allow new ideas to germinate is vital for your overall health and well-being. Rest rejuvenates.

Challenge #4: If rest doesn't happen due to your responsibilities to others, then you may begin to notice yourself seething about the demands laid upon you and blaming those around you for it. Keep in mind that the only person who can *ultimately* protect you from these demands is yourself. It may take your guy many months to get in the swing of helping you here and, even then, he's going to need reminding about what week you're on. You must help him by communicating this. If you're on your own to take care of everything, take a closer look, and see places where you can reduce or limit your load. Others really can do for themselves if you'll stop doing it for them.

Awaken and Emerge: Transitioning to Week 2, Winter

From a place of ending a cycle and beginning a new one, the New Moon gathers its self-reflection and begins to step out into the world. In the same way, your internally pointed light, which has been resting, processing, and mindfully creating, will do the same. As the week moves on, your seeds of vision will take root to grow into equally magnificent projects or enhanced relationships.

You will know you've reached the end of your **Week 1, Fall** when you awaken, step out of your dream, and find yourself deliciously invigorated and acting on your ideas. Leaving the lethargy of **Week 1,**

Release ~ Relax ~ Rejuvenate

Fall behind, barely remembering a thing about it, your fixed sense of appreciation and renewal will carry you with confidence into **Week 2, Winter**.

Adjusting the Days of This Week

Take note of how many days you tend to bleed, on average, and then observe your Mind Moods. Are you still in a quiet, visionary phase, or has that passed and you're now feeling spirited? Once you're on the move, you have transitioned into **Week 2, Winter**. How many days were you in **Week 1, Fall?**

Final Thoughts

Since my energy goes to lounging like a queen, allowing the visions in my mind to create and point my life in the direction I am being guided to go, this week has become a very exciting time for me. I am learning more and more how to let go of thoughts, perceptions, situations, and even people who cause me stress or obstruct my positive contributions to the world. I continue to grow and learn.

I encourage you to embrace the virtues and beauty of your wondrous feminine cycle. There *is* a silver lining to the dreaded, messy Period. Bless that blood every time you get it because your female hormones are Mother Nature's fountain of youth, the elixir that makes your skin and hair shine and your energy leap off the Richter scale throughout the month. It's that energy and vitality that makes you one gorgeous creature, glowing inside and out. Believe it. No matter what your childbearing capabilities are, let that blood be a reminder to you every single time you see it that *you*, my dear, are the essence of life in full bloom. The more you love it now, the more your body will remember it and maintain that rhythmic beauty once it is gone.

Release ~ Relax ~ Rejuvenate

Release ~ Relax ~ Rejuvenate

To-Do List
Week 1, Fall

Activities

- Upon awakening, take just a couple of minutes to
  - Figure out what cycle day you are on
  - Acknowledge what is basically happening with your hormones
  - Set an intention for the day regarding your health and well-being

- Lie low, get quiet, rest, and renew.

- Visualize releasing all mind, body, and spirit unhealthiness.

- Journal: Write down your thoughts, feelings, and ideas daily, or when guided.

- Allow your mind to expand with new ideas; receive spiritual guidance.

- Do some artwork or organize a drawer.

Food

Rhythmic eating is crucial for dramatically reducing uncomfortable symptoms during the first week of the feminine cycle.

- This week: Eat clean foods, fresh, organic fruits and vegetables, especially iron-rich greens; increase Omega-3s and drastically reduce sugar intake to keep inflammation down. No sugar is ideal. Get plenty of digestible protein.

Release ~ Relax ~ Rejuvenate

- ❧ Talk to your doctor about any immune-boosting supplements that could be of benefit to you. Be sure they are easy to absorb.

- ❧ Drink plenty of water and stick to warm, comforting, non-caffeinated tea. Less caffeine than usual.

Sleep

Have a boring schedule this week! Go to bed and get up at consistent times, with plenty of sleep. Remember, you are recharging your batteries here.

Exercise

In 1977 my male yoga teacher asked that his female students come to class to sit and mentally do the postures, rather than participate physically, when on their Periods. He explained that our energy needed to go to releasing. Personally, I do no exercise at all (if possible) on the first two or three days and do only the easiest versions of my routine on days four and five. I kick it into gear on days six and seven.

REMEMBER: YOU DO NOT HAVE A DISEASE AND YOU ARE NOT SICK!

If you have athletic commitments, don't hesitate to do them. Just be mellow in every other endeavor you take on, whether it's work, kids, or dinner. Don't be fooled by extra bursts of energy, as burn-out will surely sneak up on you by mid-afternoon or evening.

Relationships

Whether it is work, family, friends, or your sweetie, resist making too many dates for coffee or even phone conversations. This is quiet time for you. Think of making this your silent retreat time whenever possible. Give yourself a facial; take a long bubble bath.

Release ~ Relax ~ Rejuvenate

Sex

Do whatever suits your comfort level and that of your guy. This is a great time for sleeping sweetly skin-to-skin without engaging in much else. Happily receive massage from him and resist the urge to get too energetic yourself in order to please *him*. Toward the end of the week your juices will be dry, so learn to let bottled lubrication be your friend if you are engaging. Find a nice silky one, not sticky. Birth control is a *must* during this time if you don't want to get pregnant, even if you're still bleeding.

Personal Inquiry
Week 1, Fall

How do you feel physically this week?

What are your Mind Moods like throughout this week?

What are you doing to relax?

What are you letting go of this month that no longer serves you?

What story that you hold about yourself are you letting go of?

How are you honoring yourself?

What kinds of thoughts for the future or new ideas are you having?

Are you doing artwork or organizing?

Release ~ Relax ~ Rejuvenate

Leaves Falling

Like the tree with leaves of red
Autumn time brings letting go
Shed the old and start afresh
You are the one you need to know

Draw upon your inner self
Collect the harvest to prepare
Pamper and rejuvenate
Oh young woman ever fair

This *Sacred Bleed* from the Goddess
A time to heal and go within
Honoring with each New Moon
Relax, release and thus, begin.

—Sylvia Seroussi Chatroux, M.D.
Poetica Press

Release ~ Relax ~ Rejuvenate

The ManGuide
Week 1, Fall

"Protector"

This guide is for men who want to co-create a relationship that fills the needs of both people. The benefits are very rewarding for those who really understand and work this system, as you will see.

The "Fall" week of your sweetheart's cycle is the time to call upon the protector in you. Although you will always need to be the protector of what your partner says she wants and needs, this particular week requires more focused protection than other weeks. Show her that she can truly depend on you.

Of course, she can take care of and protect herself, but life is much easier when our partners are working with us rather than against us. And it's so sexy when our men make sure we are well cared for. The payoff for you this week is a relaxed, peaceful environment, and some free time for you. It's the perfect week for that fishing trip or puttering around at home, relaxing.

She needs rest this week, especially for the first three or four days. She isn't disabled and can still go to work and fulfill her responsibilities, but it is best if these can be done in a more relaxed way. Lounging around as much as possible is important for her. Make her a comforting dinner and bring her a glass of wine. Support this restful phase and she will appreciate it.

Her hormones are at their *lowest* while her body releases what is no longer needed. Her body is heavy and exhausted, yet her mind is expanding with innovative ideas, and a creative force takes over. Support this by keeping a circle of protection around her. She is the vessel for the sacred womb and you are, in essence, her and *its* bodyguard.

An example of this protection is to cook and care for the kids and/or home, while keeping the vibe mellow. Or, if it's more fitting to the relationship, kick back with a board game or light movie. Be cool and mellow and she'll love your support.

The idea is to get into it, to enjoy caring for her. If you get stressed or resentful yourself, then you are adding to her load, not protecting it. If she feels this happening, she may get up and take charge of everything, asking you to get out of the way. You want to display "protector" energy at all times. It's a great way for both of you to begin this new cycle.

Just prior to her Period you may have found *her* initiating sex and it might have been fast and furious. As her organs were being stimulated, energy was gathering in this area and the right environment was available for her to do any final physical releasing before going into her resting phase. Now that her Period has begun, it's best to hold back unless she says otherwise.

Rubbing her gently, or affectionate touching without *any* expectation of anything more, is the key. Avoid stimulating *anything*. Get into loving, protecting, and truly caring for and enjoying your lady by practicing sweet touch. You'll reap the benefits of experiencing deepening love for your beautiful mate. Sleeping together skin-to-skin, wrapping yourselves around each other, and stroking her back or hair are fantastic ways to deeply, sensually connect. Massaging her feet is a phenomenal way to be in service to her, and will help to balance her aches and pains. Avoid the area between her heels and ankles; this pressure point can overstimulate the uterus. Remember, intercourse comes in many different shapes and sizes. This type of connecting is a very powerful form of intercourse: *soul* intercourse.

When you display Protector energy during this week, you will love how much she'll dig and desire you. You are building a foundation for a smooth experience throughout the rest of the month.

As she finishes her Period, you may notice a quick increase in her energy and affections, *especially* since you've been caring for and protecting her. She is now entering **Week 2, Winter**, the courting and communication phase of her cycle. Clear your schedule for lots of date nights!

6. winter

Winter is the time for comfort, for good
food and warmth, for the touch of a
friendly hand and for a talk beside the
fire: it is the time for home.

—Edith Sitwell

week 2
winter

"Beautiful, Powerful Force"

KNOWN AS: The Venus Week[®18]

QUICK VIEW COMPARISONS

- ∿ **Week 2 (Days 8–14)**
- ∿ **Winter/Spring**
  - ◦ **Northern Hemisphere:** January, February, March
  - ◦ **Southern Hemisphere:** July, August, September
- ∿ **Waxing Moon**

KEY WORDS: Connective, Seductive, Lover, Productive, Brilliant in Beauty and Brains

- ∿ **Central Theme:** Building energy, relationships, projects, and sexuality
- ∿ **Focus:** Get it done now! No procrastinating
- ∿ **Symbolism:** Building up every area in your life with love and confidence
- ∿ **Intention:** Acknowledge your power and be attentive to using it often and wisely

FEMININE CYCLE

- ∿ **Hormonal Phase:** Follicular/Proliferation
- ∿ **Hormone Activity:** Estrogen building, eggs maturing, uterine walls thickening

Believe ~ Breathe ~ Become

WINTER, THE SEASON (COMPARISON)

- **In Nature:** Powerful, exciting forces: cold, snow, rain, dryness, wind; Winter Solstice to Vernal Equinox begins building light, coming out of the darkness
- **Foods:** Warm comfort food; root vegetables
- **Activity:** Productive days (inside and out) and cozy evenings

MOON (COMPARISON)

- **Phase to Relate to:** Waxing (building, growing), moving toward Full Moon
- **Moon and Feminine Cycle Phase:** Second Quarter
- **Moon and Feminine Cycle Days:** 8–14 (adjust feminine cycle days as needed)

CEREMONIAL ENERGIES

- **Four Directions:** North
- **Four Elements:** Air (communicate, breathe)
- **Colors:** Primary or true rainbow colors
- **Chakras:** Power (3), Heart (4), Sexual (2)

FEMALE BODY

- **Immune System:** Great
- **Overall Energy:** Very high
- **Physically:** Active—centered and motivated
- **Mentally:** Taking action, getting it done, super busy, yet sexually intoxicated, searching, distracted!
- **Emotional Spectrum:** Affectionate, connected, flirty, fun, confident, or yearning, pressured, depressed
- **Soulfully:** Moving from the internal Queen to the outward Goddess

Believe ~ Breathe ~ Become

- **Outward Appearance/Behavior:** Glowing, powerful, beautiful, sparkling
- **Senses:** Sound (listening, hearing), touch

SEX DRIVE

- **Juices:** Dry at first to very, very wet
- **Nipples:** Neutral to extremely responsive
- **Orgasms:** Stronger, easier, quicker
- **Ideas:** Hold hands, get cozy by the fire; allow sexual tension to build; connected lovemaking during second half of week; check out Tantra

OUTLOOK

- **Overall:** Tends to be extremely positive
- **Archetypes:** BUILDER, FUN DATE, LOVER
- **Mind Mood Persona:** "It can be done," or overly compromising due to open heart, or motivated to build relationships
- **Attitude:** Confident, sassy, fun, upbeat
- **Relationships:** Yes! Heart-to-hearts
- **When Positive:** Active, communicative, affectionate, loving
- **When Challenged:** The beginning-of-the-week "dry chill" lasts too long; depression from lack of "light," for example no ideas, no direction; feeling unattractive, no partner

SUGGESTIONS FOR YOU

- **Get busy:** Make your projects happen, build or mend your relationships
- **Make decisions and take action now:** No procrastinating

Believe ~ Breathe ~ Become

- **Make dates and be affectionate:** Connect with partner and/or friends; have fun
- **Get into being beautiful:** Build up your self-worth, image, and esteem

Care Regimen Suggestions

- **Food:** Comfort foods
- **Exercise:** YES—no excuses! Good week for weights, defining muscle
- **Sleep:** "Early to bed and early to rise" for ultimate productivity and health
- **Beauty:** Get hair done, wax, manicure, etc., at the beginning of week to set the tone for beauty, confidence, and love; you'll stand taller and feel sexier all week
- **Clothes:** Dress in your most flattering *all* the time (for you!)

Suggestions for Him

- **Courting:** This ritual needs to happen every month at this time; get into it!
- **Clear calendar** for date nights, cooking together, etc.; have fun, be interested
- **Heart-to-heart** deep talks; discuss and problem-solve relationship issues
- **Allow sexual tension** to build; be affectionate; after heart-to-hearts, turn on your best, connected lovemaking

Believe ~ Breathe ~ Become

Overview
Week 2, Winter

Week 2, Winter tends to be the most overlooked phase of the cycle by the everyday woman, yet it is a critically *important* week with which to get in touch. Because I'm excited about my hopes for the future, my communication skills are at an optimum at this time. I am eager to produce the visions I had during **Week 1, Fall**. Communicating well at this juncture sets the stage for how smoothly the rest of the month goes. It is the foundation upon which all other weeks build— the "glue" that holds it all together.

In the same way that the Moon is filling with light, you are filling with energy. Get projects done and take a few risks to make things happen, while connecting and getting cozy with your loved ones. This is, most likely, the week you'll feel your most loving, and honestly, you will need to prioritize your focus because you will want to do it all. Your enthusiasm is high and you are becoming more stunning by the minute!

Hormones
Week 2, Winter

This is the follicular phase, which means you've got a whole lot of prepping and building going on inside. You are literally a construction zone.

The Prepping: Hormones are pouring into your system from various glands and your ovaries. The hormonal scene reminds me of one of those cool science fair structural mazes where you drop a giant marble down a chute and it quickly spirals up and back, doing all kinds of acrobatic moves until it eventually tosses a cute little silver dollar pancake onto your breakfast plate.

Believe ~ Breathe ~ Become

Hormones

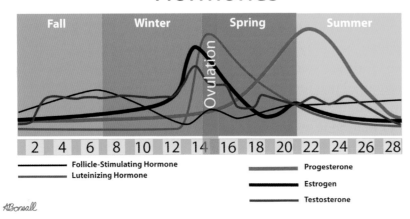

Follicle-Stimulating Hormone
Luteinizing Hormone

Progesterone

Estrogen

Testosterone

ABonsall

Instead of making hotcakes, the endometrial walls of your uterus are being thickened by all this hormonal activity. Your ovaries have been stimulated by the Follicle-Stimulating Hormone (FSH) to stimulate egg production and host a survival-of-the-fittest egg competition, sort of like a Miss Universe pageant. Only one of them will get to wear that crown and slide down the fallopian tube at Ovulation time in hopes of meeting Mr. Right.

The Construction: The main thing to keep in mind about this first half of your cycle is that your uterus is under construction. The best way I can describe it is that it is like driving by a new building site every day on your way to work. One day dirt is moved around and the next day (it seems) a foundation is being poured. Sawing and hammering is happening on the ground, and then one day you drive by and WHAM! The walls are up. It seems sort of amazing. Pretty soon the signs are going up for the business. This is the stage where your hormones are. They go from foundation at the beginning of your week to WHAM! a few days later. Instead of constructing a building, your body is creating a uterine "nest" to incubate a fertilized egg, should you become pregnant. The walls of your uterus are up now, so to speak, thickening, and just starting to hang out the sign for the fertilized egg to come on in and nest.

Your estrogen is really spiking during this week, going from being

Believe ~ Breathe ~ Become

a foundation at floor level to the wall being erected. This all happens over a matter of seven to 10 days or so, from the time you end your Period to the time the egg gets released from the ovary, which is *Ovulation*. Not only does estrogen thicken the wall of your uterus, it also lubricates your moving parts. It is the hormone (along with testosterone) that jump-starts all kinds of healthy action in your body, including your libido. Just as your estrogen goes from foundation to wall, your sex drive spikes in tandem right along with it. Low and dry to high and wet, all in one week. You may have wanted sex during your Period or not, or you may want sex as soon as you begin to warm up, but since your communication is great during this time, I suggest getting in your talks, connecting, and affectionate dates during the first half of this week to make sure they happen. Then allow yourself to enjoy getting physical during the second half.

Estrogen peaks somewhere around Day 12, 13, or 14, which activates the egg-releasing process called Ovulation. It can take 24 to 36 hours for the egg to burst out of the ovary. Once this happens we begin **Week 3, Spring**. In the 4s4w strategy, **Week 3, Spring** *begins* with Ovulation.

Your Rhythm and The Pill:

Your hormones are not going to hit the same high peak as they would without The Pill, because most birth control is set up to prevent Ovulation from happening. Check with your health practitioner about The Pill you are using. Do not let this keep you from being magnanimous anyway! If you are on The Pill, this tells me you are most likely in a relationship, or you would like one. Perhaps you are on The Pill to regulate your hormones. Follow the 4s4w suggestions anyway. You may be suppressing your ability to conceive, but there is no reason to keep yourself from enjoying the benefits of the female rhythm. Attract your man and allow him to court you. Your estrogen and testosterone will be lower than when not on The Pill, which may keep you from feeling *as* frisky, but sex is mostly a mental game. Let your mind take over where your hormones leave off to fuel your female rhythm. Just knowing you are protected against pregnancy can be enough to

Believe ~ Breathe ~ Become

keep you sexier than ever and vibrantly magnetic. Get in there and enjoy this week, as well as the time when Ovulation would normally happen, because you are in the great position of not worrying about conceiving! If you follow the 4s4w blueprint, you'll find your *mental sex rhythm* will support your sex drive just fine.

Fertility Awareness: If You Are *Not* on The Pill

Birth control is an absolute *must* during this entire week if you do not want to become pregnant. Sperm can live inside of you for up to seven days,[19] waiting for a chance to connect with your "Beauty Queen" egg at Ovulation time. I can't say BIRTH CONTROL or CONTRACEPTION enough times here. If you are not on some form of The Pill, have an IUD, or have your tubes tied, you'll want to use another type of birth control, CORRECTLY, starting way back in **Week 1, Fall**. Like me, you may be an early ovulator (I ovulate on Day 11 or 12), so leave absolutely nothing to chance if you do not want a pregnancy. Make sure your guy understands this concept and do not, *under any circumstances*, buckle on this. Stand firm no matter how much you're wanting him, or he you. Pregnancies *do* happen even when you think you are being mindful. Knowledge is the key.

I've got three children from using birth control incorrectly. We were using it too late in my cycle for it to prevent the sperm from hanging out in my Queen Egg's waiting room. It worked out well that my life was in a solid enough place to handle the pregnancies and to be a good mom. Are you in that place? If you're not, taking a risk by getting caught up in the moment, and then consciously deciding you'll deal with a pregnancy later, should it occur, is unacceptable and irresponsible behavior. Get clear NOW about your birth control method. Get disciplined on how you are going to implement it *before* your brains and loins get wobbly, so that your response will be automatic and strong when it is needed most. If the guy you're with criticizes you for being responsible about birth control, it is time to do some serious evaluating of your relationship and possibly end it now, before you end up with a child together. Be your own protector.

Believe ~ Breathe ~ Become

Reproduction Comparison: Courting Phase

Week 2, Winter is the week I compare to the Courting Phase, because this is the week we are attracting a mate before Ovulation occurs.

Our estrogen and testosterone are rising rapidly, making sure that we are glowing like Venus de Milo in order to attract and co-mingle, while our wombs are busy preparing a nest for a possible pregnancy. This is the week for fun dates, heart-to-heart talks, and affection between couples, in order to develop deep and ongoing attraction. It is the week of romance. This time of courting every single month is a crucial ritual to keep alive if you want your love connection to stay alive. This is the savings account into which you both are depositing trust, kindness, connection, agreements, safety, and fun times. If this account becomes depleted, you won't have anything to draw on during the challenging moments or stretches. This account must always be kept in high standing.

For deeper understanding of this week and more ideas on how to truly claim it, I recommend, as a must read, Dr. Rebecca Booth's *The Venus Week: Discover the Powerful Secret of Your Cycle… At Any Age.*[20] Named after the Roman goddess of Love, Beauty, and Fertility, our active hormones turn us into nothing less than the ultimate Goddess during this phase.

Characteristics
Week 2, Winter

Reminder: The 4s4w strategy, or system, was created for the sole purpose of putting the feminine cycle into perspective in order to relate our experiences to its week-to-week and day-to-day changes and remembering how they go without too much effort.

Each woman is different and ultimately must identify and adjust

Believe ~ Breathe ~ Become

her own rhythm, but the hormonal influences of each phase tend to have the same general characteristics as the seasons. The 4s4w system attempts to add meaning to these characteristics.

The Feminine Cycle (Days 8–14)

This week starts out with a lot of energy. Venturing out of your hormonal flatlands, where you were lying low in **Week 1, Fall**, you're now rested up and ready for your estrogen to take you on the most exhilarating adventure of your cycle. You've come upon **Week 2, Winter**, a breathtaking snowy mountain, glistening in the Sun, rising to the highest peak, the point that *stimulates* Ovulation (**Week 3, Spring**). With estrogen rising rapidly, your inner and outer brilliance radiates exponentially as these hormones prepare your uterus for possible pregnancy. Your sex drive is going from 0 to 100.

Just like when climbing a mountain, you'll go through many different changes in scenery, because of changing elevation, in a short amount of time. Your juices will go from their driest to their wettest this week, starting out in the desert and ascending to the mountain rainforest or sparkling snow-topped peak in a matter of just a few days. Like beeswax heating up, you'll start out feeling a bit solid until all of your muscles and tissues begin to melt, becoming delicious, warm, and gooey honey.

How the *Characteristics* of Winter, the Moon, and the Feminine Cycle Relate

Days and Nights: The Winter Solstice signals the Sun to bring us out of the darkness by beginning to lengthen the amount of light per day. Like the waxing Moon breaking out of the darkness of the New Moon, you are breaking out of your cocoon of lying low during your Period and building brilliance day by day.

Taking Action: January 1st is the day we begin to implement our New Year's resolutions. We feel motivated to take action toward losing weight, making more money, creating more time for ourselves, or perhaps meditating more.

Believe ~ Breathe ~ Become

The Bridge: Winter is the bridge between Fall and Spring, when we catch our breath and get things back to a routine after the whirlwind of holidays. This gives us the opportunity to get indoor projects done before we'll want to spend time outdoors in Spring and Summer. This bridge is the transition in your cycle from the lowest hormones to the highest, preparing you for the Spring Party: Ovulation.

Powerful Beauty: The sparkling snow is captivating and breathtaking, yet it can keep us from getting out of our driveways. Cold air is invigorating, yet it can chill us to the bone. Fierce Winter storms knock out electricity for days and shut down cities, yet they can bring people together in their troubles, reminding us that Mother Nature can be magnificent and dangerous. Just like women. Just like you.

Connections: Winter can be a very active time if you're a snowboarder, but of all the seasons, Winter is the indoor task time, the home and hearth time. When not working, we spend time cooking together, getting cozy by the fire, or watching movies. It's family time. It is the time when we meet our friends for coffee for both the warmth of the beverage and the warmth of our hearts. This phase of your cycle, **Week 2, Winter**, gives you the same opportunity to be the nurturing lover, friend, or mother. Connecting warmly during this week, in this way, is *imperative* for a smoother feminine cycle month.

At all costs, avoid the temptation to be the nurturing mother to your lover during this phase. It's not sexy—it's creepy. Treat him like your hunky, protective man. Let him court you and allow yourself to be treated like the hottest woman on the planet. You are.

Valentines: Sensually, these long, cold nights invite us to crave skin-to-skin contact with our partners to keep us safe and warm. Pressing into the heat of another's body during this time can be an especially erotic mixing under the sheets. Minds and souls cross over the physical limitations to step inside and reach into each other's core in an attempt to exchange warmth. Two people become one. Hearts find each other during this Winter holiday called Valentine's Day and throughout this phase of your cycle.

Believe ~ Breathe ~ Become

> **Feelings of neutrality, power, affection, and beauty** in Winter are similar to feelings experienced in Week 2, Winter of the feminine cycle, which tends to be the best phase for building personable connections as well as stoking the fire under your romantic relationship.

Symbolic Transitions & Influences
Week 2, Winter

Since **Week 2, Winter** is part of a cycle in motion, the first day of the week is different from the last day of the week. Our physical bodies *and* our Mind Moods change daily.

Influences on the Body: Building Sexuality

- Dry to wet
- Productive/Active
- Heartfelt, cooperative
- Sexually intoxicated and intoxicating

By the time **Week 2, Winter** gets here, the shedding of the uterus via blood is completed. The transition from Week 1 to Week 2 is a soft one, meaning there is no real marker day. You'll identify the beginning of **Week 2, Winter** once you have eased out of your Period and know that you're done. If you still feel low and slow, you are still in **Week 1, Fall**. If you are feeling finished with your visioning and eager to get moving, then you have stepped into **Week 2, Winter**. This could be anywhere from Day 4 to Day 8, depending on what is normal for you. Keep in mind that, for the sake of the 4s4w tem-

Believe ~ Breathe ~ Become

plate, I divide 28 days into four equal weeks of seven days each, and therefore I use Day 8 as the first day of Week 2. However, you may discover that your Week 1 is made up of six days and your Week 2 is nine days, for instance. The 4s4w strategy is a general template for everyone to start with, but MUST be customized for you. You are unique and your monthly cycle will also vary at times. With consistent daily tracking, you'll begin to see your pattern. This is extremely easy and takes almost no time.

Our bodies and juices are dry after coming off our Periods, just as our faces and hands are dry when the harsh cold of Winter hits. Just as I feel a little relieved to be done with the holidays, I always feel relieved to be done with my Period. I am very energized yet calm, and my brain is very active with tasks. I feel balanced all the way around and exceptionally free to do whatever I want. This balanced feeling makes me feel good physically, and when I feel good physically it's a perfect time for taking action on projects and connecting with others at home or at work.

As if feeling good isn't enough, Mother Nature's best beauty secret, estrogen, builds in our systems. This phenomenal emollient moisturizes and plumps our skin, hair, nipples, and lips (above *and* below). Ready or not, this intoxicating lubricant is beautifying everything about you, making you into one hot babe inside and out. It's as if I can literally feel the hormones racing through my blood and, as the week wears on, I can get quite distracted by having sex on the brain. You'll feel yourself getting antsy to get out and mingle.

As this week builds, you'll glow with magnetic charm and personality, radiating confidence. *Allow* yourself to dress better than usual. Ask for anything you want during this week and you'll probably get it. Have fun being flirty, communicative, in charge, and affectionate.

Believe ~ Breathe ~ Become

Influences on the Mind and Soul: Beauty and Brains

Mind Moods and ARCHETYPES

- Preparing for Ovulation, the "Spring Party"
- BUILDER: Home and Hearth, Communicating, Nurturing
- FUN DATE: Affection, Romance, Courtship
- LOVER: Seductive, Radiant Beauty
- Anticipation

Preparing for Ovulation, the "Spring Party"

We spend a lot of time in Winter catching up on projects and chores in order to be ready when Spring hits. We are fully aware that our minds will be in a different place when the weather is at its nicest.

The same thing happens with your cycle. **Week 2, Winter** is the prep or foreplay for **Week 3, Spring**. Ovulation is the "Spring Party," the event you throw inside your body every month at midpoint. Without this party to plan for, there would be no reason for a cycle.

Our entire sexual society is driven by attraction to this *most attractive force field in the Universe*. It is the sanctuary to where emotions and sex drives make a pilgrimage every month. We lead and men follow. Ovulation is the destination. It is an Alpha and Omega. It is orgasm at its most orgasmic. It is spirituality at its zenith. Ovulation is your purest truth. Ovulation is your highest self, your vastest possibility. It is the vista of the world from atop the highest mountain.

If you are *not* an ovulating woman because of hysterectomy or menopause, do not despair. You can consciously recreate this rhythm because your female body is set up to support it—rhythm is what it knows. Just because you are not fertile ground for a baby does *not* mean you are not fertile ground for a magnetic sexual relationship or the best projects of your life. By tracking using the Moon phases, beginning with the New Moon, you'll discover that your body has not forgotten the way, even if you are no longer reproductive. Your body has many energetic cycles within its rhythm and you may find your

Believe ~ Breathe ~ Become

Mind Moods, your physical energy, *and* your sex drive (because of what it remembers) may not have changed all that much. Make adjustments with lubrication and your attitude and, by all means, allow yourself to be courted. Allow your rhythm to be fueled by your mind, intuition, and habit, rather than by your hormones.

BUILDER: Home and Hearth, Communicator, Nurturer

Because your hormones are constructing a nest, your energy is also building, becoming a well-oiled machine practically overnight. The excitement that happens when an idea is being brought to fruition is the same excitement you'll feel during **Week 2, Winter**, because this is the week to make your projects happen, to bring them to fruition. You are building your future. You are building your dreams. Your projects may be work-related, home-related, or relationship-related.

When your thoughts, words, and actions line up, clarity is the result. It will construct or deconstruct a project or relationship very quickly. When they do not line up you will find yourself stuck, bored, lost, or feeling victimized and used. It's very easy to move around in life with absolutely no awareness of where you're going or what you're manifesting with your actions or inactions. Begin to make it a priority to figure out what it is you really want your future to look like and begin walking in that direction. Begin by noticing if your thoughts, words, and actions line up.

If you're clear, you may find yourself jumping right into taking your ideas from the previous week and making them happen, or continuing an ongoing project. Go for it! Confidence is on your side and others can feel it—this is a powerful force. Acknowledge what you're doing well and how capable you are.

If you're not quite sure, you may find yourself getting stressed. Your hormones and energy are moving forward to support your endeavors, whether you are ready or not. The stress you feel could be an underlying pressure to get it together and make decisions. Move your intentions forward with action.

I've finally learned to recognize this week as the one to get things

> Everyone has been made for some particular work, and the desire for that work has been put in every heart. Let yourself be silently drawn by the stronger pull of what you really love.
>
> —Rumi

Believe ~ Breathe ~ Become

done and to make important decisions *now*. No procrastinating!

This second week of the feminine cycle is the time when I have my best "people" hat on, networking in every area of my life, business, friends, and home. This is the week I attract positive people and things into my life.

The time to connect is *now*! Have the conversations that need to be had, especially if you've been journaling, listing your pet peeves, or just whatever needs to be worked out. This is especially true for committed couples. It is crucial that you have heart-to-hearts at the beginning of this week before you hit your most optimal physical time together.

Having good communication here, discussing the things that have been on your mind, is crucial for experiencing a smoother **Week 4, Summer** (the traditional PMS week) two weeks later. It's time now to name your unhappiness to prevent a build-up of negativity or anger month after month, year after year. Discuss the things you need to discuss now. Make opportunities to connect.

Think of all of this communicating and dating as foreplay for the end of the week and the beginning of **Week 3, Spring**. Great communication is a real turn-on and makes for the best kind of connection. You'll learn to really like each other if you practice active speaking, listening, and *hearing*.

Week 2, Winter is a cozy, touchy/feely week—the week to "feel the love." Give lots of hugs and tell your family and friends you love them. Be affectionate with your honey. Get into cooking nutritious comfort foods for everyone. Take the time to spend quality time whenever you can and with whomever you need to spend it. Appreciate.

Believe ~ Breathe ~ Become

Fun Date: Affection, Romance and Courtship

Include your guy, if you have one, for the most positive 4s4w experience possible. This is crucial for receiving every possible benefit of your rhythm! Women I have surveyed say that having their feminine cycles understood is second only to feeling healthy on a regular basis. The 4s4w system is one that guys totally "get." Share this book with yours.

Take him on this journey so that he can understand the benefits to *you* as well as to *himself* and, ultimately, to the *relationship*. **Week 2, Winter** is the week he needs to be willing to participate in having fun, actively connecting, and communicating well. Share what day you are on in your cycle in order for him to synchronize with you.

Clear the decks for long talks and affection building, especially during the first half of the week. Again, if there is something you've been wanting or needing to talk about, this is the week to do it. Although you may find yourself wanting to go the sexual distance, see if you can focus on your communication and affectionate physicality more than your carnal physicality—mainly because this is your best

Believe ~ Breathe ~ Become

chance to communicate well from the heart. Feeling peaceful, happy, and confident makes your wise words easier to hear and makes *you* more receptive to what he has to say.

Ask him to leave his week open for date nights. Plan to do some fun things because, in my opinion and experience, fun is the key to opening a man's heart. Most guys I know are always up for a good time. Go with what *he* likes (and of course what you enjoy): Play video games or air hockey. Take photo booth pictures. Go dancing or to a comedy night. Go river rafting, mountain biking, camping, or dirt bike riding. You could probably use a little fun yourself! Do non-serious stuff in order to play with your partner. If you get a little fun under your belt, heart-to-heart talks are much easier to initiate. Long walks are a good place to begin. Avoid alcohol or other altering influences in order to keep things real.

> *Never stop trying to win the heart of the person you're in love with.*
> —Nik Martin

- ꕥ Fun stuff
- ꕥ Hold hands
- ꕥ Long walks
- ꕥ Great talks

In that order. Believe me, this is a good plan.

So you say you want a real man? Get into the art of courtship. *He's* courting *you*, so let him! Get into relaxing a bit and let somebody *else* do the work for a change. Let him open your car door and you'll discover how sexy that is. If he's not in the habit of courting, let him know during your heart-to-hearts what you would like. It doesn't need to get silly—if you're in a hurry and need to hop in, then open the door yourself and hop in—go with what feels natural, but otherwise enjoy this courting dance. If he is the right and healthy guy for you, then expect to be courted, showing him where your boundaries are for being with you. If you want him to continue, you must not slack off on showing your approval and desire for *him*.

Courting is *not* a one-time activity. No matter how many years you've been together, this needs to happen every single month during every single year you are together! EVERY SINGLE MONTH! Court-

Believe ~ Breathe ~ Become

ing eventually goes both directions and works best during the second week of the female sex cycle. You are both responsible for keeping the spark alive in your relationship for you both to stay happy and content in it. This is a dance of respect, honor, and equality. You are a Queen and, with the right rhythmic movement, you will find your King—the guy you actually love to hang out with.

Deep connections can be made by hanging out and snuggling up at the fireplace (or fire pit) and actually enjoying each other—sweet kisses, holding hands, listening to music, and cooking together. This may seem obvious, but being consistent and regular about this, as well as timing it to be in sync with your cycle, is rarely done and makes all the difference to a relationship. This is conscious connecting and conscious living. It may take many months to get this **Week 2, Winter** right, but it is crucial that you do in order for the whole month to go more smoothly, especially the fourth week, the Fire Walk (the traditional PMS week). If you, as a couple, get good at honoring the weekly cycle assignments, you'll find affection flowing between the two of you throughout the entire month.

LOVER: Seductive, Radiant Beauty

We begin **Week 2, Winter** as fun, connected, and more cute than gorgeous. Over the course of a few days we transform into stunning, erotic creatures (inside and out, and in our own way) until we reach Ovulation, where we explode into magnificence. We are the light that attracts. We are men's obsessions. We are leaders and rulers.

As you become more brilliant in your look, your presence, and your appeal, you'll need to keep your wits about you while also allowing yourself to shine. You've become a sex magnet, from a biological point of view. If you need to create offspring for the good of the village, then Nature is providing you with the tools to do so. If there are already too many mouths to feed, then you have been given the brains to resist sex or to make sure reliable birth control is in place. In the past, this meant the use of herbs or some other local form of preventative barrier.

Believe ~ Breathe ~ Become

This is easier said than done, as you are irresistible to your partner at this phase, and you are probably feeling quite willing to co-mingle. You look beautiful, you feel beautiful, and your sexual craving may be quite strong. Your seductive cat is on the prowl and you *will* land your prey.

This is where your work on your clarity comes in: getting as close to your pure truth about your values and principles *beforehand* is crucial for handling this well. You don't want to end up with the wrong guy, or allow a pregnancy to happen when you do not want one.

Anticipation: Transitioning to Week 3, Spring

In **Week 1, Fall** we went inward, just as the New Moon keeps its light to itself. During **Week 2, Winter** our hormones spent time building a nest, pushing our energy, beauty, confidence, and sexuality outward in the same way that the Moon grows bigger and brighter by the day. By the time we get to **Week 3, Spring**, we will be at our most magnificent, receiving light, extending our most glorious shine for all to see, like the Full Moon herself.

Anticipation seems to be a subconscious thing that happens before any big event. It's the piece that makes your energy feel a little

Believe ~ Breathe ~ Become

frantic. It's the longing and emotional tug-o'-war between getting the party started and feeling nervous that you're not quite ready. There is a hope and a prayer that everything will go as planned and dreamed.

When brought to the surface, anticipation is step one of your *expectations*. This is the stage when you are visualizing how you *want* things to go or how you naturally *see them* going. It's the angst I feel in the pit of my stomach when I'm leaning into the mirror to put on my eyeliner before going out on the town, preparing for a speaking engagement, or simply needing to be at my best, socially and publicly.

Pre-Ovulation is the stage in your cycle when *anticipation builds* right up to the moment that the egg is released, whether you know it is happening or not. Something primal is occurring, and that something will be answered when Ovulation is over. Will your soul feel satisfied or let down afterward?

> **Challenge #1:** You may find, because your heart is open and you're feeling good, beautiful, and successful, that you've over-compromised, saying yes to things you wish you hadn't. It's really okay to go back and revisit an earlier conversation. Stand in your truth when you have new thoughts, new insights, or a fresh perspective.

Adjusting the Days of This Week

You may find that your Winter Week begins earlier or later than I suggest. If you have a shorter Period, take note of when you go from being internal to breaking out of that shell and stepping into a new phase. Track your Winter Week as starting then. By tracking over time, or by paying attention to your physical experience and mental attitude during these weeks, you will begin to identify your transition days from one "season" to another. Excellent! Congratulate yourself for tuning in to YOU!

Believe ~ Breathe ~ Become

Final Thoughts

If you are not used to stepping into your beauty, power, flirtatious sexuality, or peace-making skills, go for it during this week. Your hormones are the wind beneath your wings, so to speak. During **Week 1, Fall** you were lounging around and living in your sweats or pjs whenever possible. Start **Week 2, Winter** by doing your nails, getting body waxed, or your hair shaped. Wear your best clothes for the occasion throughout this entire week. I ALWAYS feel more successful when I dress better. You don't have to go out and buy new stuff. Begin putting yourself together a little differently with a bit more attention. Don't be afraid to try something new. Be beautiful!

Believe ~ Breathe ~ Become

To-Do List
Week 2, Winter

Activities

- ∾ Upon awakening, take just a couple of minutes to
  - Figure out what cycle day you are on
  - Acknowledge what is basically happening with your hormones
  - Set an intention for the day regarding your health and well-being

- ∾ Prioritize your projects; make lists.

- ∾ Get started on your beauty regimen; clean up nails, hair, etc.

- ∾ Connect with loved ones.

- ∾ Focus on communication and affection with your sweetheart.

- ∾ Allow your self-esteem to expand and your beauty to glow.

Food

Comfort food works great for me during this week. Your body is strong here. This doesn't mean go crazy. If you want to be healthy and feel well, then you already know a balanced diet is a must. I'm saying that if you want to make cookies or have sauces over your veggies, then this is the week to have at it. Decide what is right for you. See 4s4w's *Food for a Female Planet* for more info.

Sleep

Just get your normal amount in here. Try to be consistent with the times you go to bed and get up for optimal results.

Believe ~ Breathe ~ Become

Exercise

Your energy is building every day and you should be taking advantage of it with no excuses. Think of it as being in training for **Week 3, Spring**. Build up your body and your endurance here. Varied forms of exercise need to be a priority during this week.

Relationships

This is a great time to have coffee with friends and get into being a team player at work. With your sweetie, go on long walks, have great talks, snuggle up, enjoy sweet lovemaking, and sleep skin to skin.

Sex

My suggestion for the first half of this week is to let the sexual tension build and spend most of your focus on communication and dates. Try this for a few rounds of your cycle to see what happens. If you decide to go for it, keep in mind that, physically, women are somewhat vaginally dry after bleeding. All the lubrication has left your body during the previous week, so you may not feel like initiating or even receiving sex right off. Bottled lubrication is a miracle in my book, a true magic elixir sent from Heaven that can flip that switch from off to on. Give it a try and see what you think. Some are silkier than others and, even though the silky ones are more expensive, you'll love the difference immediately! Avoid the sticky ones—they don't glide and are messy.

You will most likely discover that, as your estrogen kicks in, bursts of intense sexuality will hit you. Remember, you are very fertile during this week. If you and your guy can't talk about birth control, don't have sex. No glove, no love, as they say.

> **Challenge #2.** Be careful not to allow the coldness to go on too long. Because you are drier down below, your libido may be hibernating. Once you've gone a few cycle rounds of getting the communication thing down and your relationship improves, give yourself permission to wake that sleeping giant.

Believe ~ Breathe ~ Become

Personal Inquiry
Week 2, Winter

How do you feel physically this week?

What are your *Mind Moods*?

What projects are you creating?

Are you feeling successful at their progress?

What are your desires for your relationships this week?

Do you feel sexier than usual?

Are you dressing up?

If you have a love interest, is he courting you the way you'd like to be courted?

What do you love about the way he is courting you?

What would you like for him to be doing in addition to or instead of?

Are you responding to him by making an effort to raise the vibration of your connection by looking nicer and being a little more open to his offers?

What else do you notice about this week?

Believe ~ Breathe ~ Become

Venus Ruling

Like the waxing of the Moon
Feminine strength and you shall shine
With your power to create
Prepare the seed in Winter time

Venus rules this time of year
Love and strength combine in grace
You can build and connect
Powerful, create your place

Proliferation makes a home
Where one could grow and
    one can sing
Building up with energy
Winter time shall lead to Spring.

—Sylvia Seroussi Chatroux, M.D.
Poetica Press

Believe ~ Breathe ~ Become

The ManGuide

Week 2, Winter

"Hot Boyfriend"

This is the week of communication, deep connection, and fun, loving affection. You get to tap in to that excited place you were at when you first met her, when you were becoming boyfriend and girlfriend. Remember how attentive you were to her needs and how you wanted to know everything about her? Remember how you asked her out on dates, showed up on time, thought about what you wore, and went the extra mile to apply after-shave? Maybe even cleaned out, washed, and vacuumed your car? The most important thing I can tell you about creating, participating in, and maintaining a great relationship is this: courting needs to happen all month long, and throughout the entirety of your relationship. This is the first step to making love to a woman really, really well and *this* week, **Week 2, Winter**, is when her chemistry would like to align with yours more than anything. And YOU get to have fun, be romantic, and feel *her* support for *you*!

Consider this to be date week. The theme of this week is fun, connection, and affection. It is vital that you take this opportunity to do some serious, and not so serious, bonding. Begin with lots of hand-holding and going places together, just hanging out. Plan at least one nice dinner out together (without the kids, if there are any). If money is a challenge, go for something inexpensive, but make it special in some way. Courting means that YOU get to do the planning and arranging. She will really appreciate your efforts and you will feel good about stepping up to the plate. The rewards for both of you are closer intimacy, playfulness, and a regular reminder of why you fell in love. Enjoy it!

The heart is what rules this week and it is important to develop monthly heart-to-heart talks. Make notes throughout the month of what you want to talk about and share them at this time. In addition to discussing information and concerns, express your love and gratitude to each other and share your vulnerabilities. It is amazing what this can do to strengthen your fondness for each other, and your ability to work as a team. You'll get another chance to connect well with "mind-to-mind" talks after Ovulation, during **Week 3, Spring**.

Your honey is motivated and has many things happening this week. She is building relationships and implementing projects. Mostly, she has her man, *you*, on her mind. We're really talking about primal responses here that she may not be aware of. If you want this week to turn into a sexually physical one, then making sweet connections with her is the ticket. Remember, courting is a form of foreplay.

If you haven't already, talk together about birth control. Choose the method that works best for both of you.

You will have the opportunity to be the hero and protector of your lady in a variety of ways throughout the month by aligning with her rhythmic sex cycle at each step. Last week, **Fall**, you supported her in her efforts to rest and rejuvenate. This week is about showing her that you support her projects, enjoy being with her, that you feel honored to be the man in her life, and are excited about opportunities to connect "heartfully" and physically with her and only her.

This week, more than any other, her sexuality is going from zero to one hundred. Show up as her *man* and she will want you! Make this the sexiest week of the month by enjoying the intoxication of being in love and being the attentive lover. By the end of the week you should be howling at the Moon!

7. spring

May, The Hare Moon

Now is the time to celebrate life and love.
Renew and affirm your sensuality, kindle
the fire of romance. Dance and make love
by the light of a bonfire, the glow of red
candles, or just the Full Moon's radiance.
Free your wild nature.

—Author Unknown

week 3
spring
"Fertile Flowing Spirit"

KNOWN AS: Ovulation

QUICK VIEW COMPARISONS

- **Week 3 (Days 15–21)**
- **Spring/Summer**
  - **Northern Hemisphere:** April, May, June
  - **Southern Hemisphere:** October, November, December
- **Full Moon**

KEY WORDS: Sexual, Physical, Primal, Potent, Fearless, Innocent/Experienced, Enlightened

- **Central Theme:** Putting your full self of light and love out for all to benefit
- **Focus:** Sacred sexuality, passion, pregnancy (or not)
- **Symbolism:** Your projects or efforts have come to fruition and you have attracted others to be interested; spotlight your ideas and thoughts; release your inhibitions
- **Intention:** To use good judgment while not holding back

FEMININE CYCLE

- **Hormonal Phase:** Ovulatory
- **Hormone Activity:** Egg is released from the ovary into the fallopian tube for fertilization

Express ~ Enchant ~ Enlighten

Spring, the Season (comparison)

- **In Nature:** Rain, green, bursting growth, flowers, early vegetables and fruit; Vernal Equinox to the Summer Solstice builds to the longest, lightest day of the year

- **Foods:** Early fruits and vegetables loaded with fresh flavor

- **Activity:** Everyone outdoors! Planting gardens, baseball, cleaning out garages

Moon (comparison)

- **Phase to Relate to:** FULL!

- **Moon and Feminine Cycle Phase:** Midpoint/halfway

- **Moon and Feminine Cycle Days:** 15–21 (adjust Week 3 to begin at Ovulation)

Ceremonial Energies

- **Four Directions:** East

- **Four Elements:** Water (lubricated; adaptable)

- **Colors:** Greens, pastels, or colors muted with grey

- **Chakras:** Crown (7), Sexual (2), Power (3)

Female Body

- **Immune System:** Great

- **Overall Energy:** Very high

- **Physically:** External, extending, open, physical, blood pulsing, heavier breathing, and then satisfied, *or* stressed and dissatisfied

- **Mentally:** Sexually focused on caught prey, wild and adventurous, and then clear, wise, and powerful, *or* obsessed

- **Emotional Spectrum:** Confident to vulnerable, expecting to be admired and desired, but could get rejected or disap-

Express ~ Enchant ~ Enlighten

pointed, to feeling very solid during second half of week

- **Soulfully:** Sexy, anxious, willing, upbeat, affectionate, conquering
- **Outward Appearance/Behavior:** Hot, powerful, erotic, mesmerizing, colorful
- **Senses:** Smell, taste

SEX DRIVE

- **Juices:** Dripping wet and elastic, backing off after Ovulation
- **Nipples:** Extremely responsive, reaching, stimulated
- **Orgasms:** Stronger, easier, quicker
- **Ideas:** Go for it! Try something new; primal acts rule over lovemaking for the first day or two; bask in the afterglow for the rest of the week, resuming regular physicality while discussing sex: what worked, what didn't, with honor and kindness for each other

OUTLOOK

- **Overall:** Could be positive or negative
- **Archetypes:** GODDESS (sexually and spiritually), WISE WOMAN, WORLD LEADER
- **Mind Mood Persona:** "Here I am," and "Here's how we take care of this," balanced, wise, brave
- **Attitude:** Bold, fearless, risky, primal, spiritual
- **Relationships:** Physical, electrically connected, intoxicating
- **When Positive:** Sexual, willing, high self-esteem, fun, in full creation mode
- **When Challenged:** Don't feel well, can't focus on tasks, not satisfied, low feminine self-esteem, lonely, depressed, judging self or others, jealous, arrogant, unhappy, disappointed

Express ~ Enchant ~ Enlighten

SUGGESTIONS FOR YOU

- **Express your primal sexuality:** time to get down and dirty—birth control a must

- **Shine!** Break out of your cocoon and express yourself, present your passions

- **Be open** to learning and trying something new, being vulnerable, and reviewing it later

- **Allow yourself** to let go, relax, surrender, and enjoy the party!

- **Engage** in connected mind-to-mind evaluation of your relationships after Ovulation

CARE REGIMEN SUGGESTIONS

- **Food:** Flavorful, colorful, juicy, and healthy

- **Exercise:** Yes!

- **Sleep:** What?

- **Beauty:** Knock 'em dead

- **Clothes:** Naughty lingerie in the house—no borrowing a cup of sugar from the neighbor unless it's your boyfriend! Tasteful style in public

SUGGESTIONS FOR HIM

- **Sexually:** Get primal, be her animal, adore and revere her, howl at the Moon, satisfy your hunger (birth control a must), let her see your devotion to her alone

- **Be open** to learning, being vulnerable, and trying something new; CONNECT

- **Be willing,** after Ovulation, to discuss sex and discovered desires of both of you; participate in mind-to-mind communication, perfecting your synchronization with her cycle

Express ~ Enchant ~ Enlighten

Overview
Week 3, Spring

Week 3, Spring begins with *Ovulation*: the guiding light and magnetic force of Spring fever and your entire feminine cycle. You are at your sexiest, flirtiest, and most magnanimous. One ripe egg is ready to receive sperm and the cavewoman in you has been doing your darnedest to attract some. As the Full Moon is receptive to the full light of the Sun, you are receptive to the full light of the sexual energy from your partner, or the hope or potential of a partner.

Your sexual energy might instead be channeled through projects, sports, art, or events. Whatever your focus, like the Full Moon extending her fullest expression, this is the time to fully express yourself by presenting your goods, giving out and reaping the undivided attention of those who want and deserve to experience what you have to offer. You are fearless and vulnerable, experienced and innocent, receiving and attracting, all at the same time, radiating your own superb glow.

As if that isn't enough, your magnificence continues once Ovulation is done, with your most impressive qualities yet to come. Wisely reflecting upon your personal as well as global circumstances, your nurturing, problem-solving, world-view nature could make you the most sought-after consultant on the planet.

Hormones
Week 3, Spring

Ovulation is midpoint in the monthly cycle. It is the time when one beautiful egg gets released from an ovary with the goal of connecting with one hunky sperm.

Right away, as we enter **Week 3, Spring**, we are peaking just as

Express ~ Enchant ~ Enlighten

the Full Moon peaks. The Full Moon is only truly full for one day, and you will only ovulate on one day, meaning fertilization is possible only during a 24- to 36-hour period. However, please keep in mind that your fertile day, *unlike* the Full Moon, can be an unpredictable moving target.

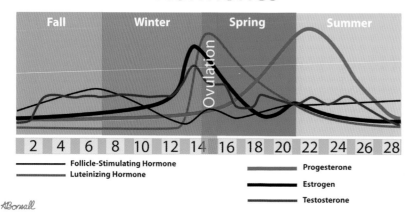

Just as the Full Moon is opposite from the New Moon, Ovulation, *in a perfect world,* is at the opposite point in your cycle from the first day of your Period, thus happening on Day 14 or 15. All of this can vary greatly from woman to woman. *You* could actually ovulate somewhere between Days 11 and 21.[21]

Remember, for the sake of teaching you the **basic** 4s4w strategy, I am using a 28-day model, divided into four equal weeks of seven days each, which has Ovulation Day landing on Day 15. Once you get the basic idea down, you'll need to adjust the days in each seasonal week to fit the unique *you* and begin **Week 3, Spring** on the day you ovulate, *whenever* that is.

The general rule of thumb is that the Period comes 14 days later, but studies are showing it can be anywhere from 12 to 16 days after.[22] Tracking your cycle becomes important in order to understand *your* individual rhythm. Even then, knowing exactly when you ovulate can

Express ~ Enchant ~ Enlighten

be tricky. Easy instructions for basic tracking are included later in this book, but getting to know your Ovulation day takes more study. Checking your mucus/juices and taking your temperature is one way to know when you're ovulating. Another way is to use an "Ovulation kit," which can be purchased online. I'm pretty good at detecting when I ovulate because I'm one of the lucky 20 percent who gets a big twinge or cramp in my ovary (sometimes the right side, sometimes the left) when the egg is released. It's uncomfortable, but now that I know more about Ovulation, I appreciate the signal.

The Turning Point

The Follicle-Stimulating Hormone (FSH) did its job during the first half of your cycle and stimulated follicles in your ovaries to develop mature eggs.[23]

Your ovaries are basically like one of those lottery popcorn machines holding ping-pong balls with numbers on them. As the balls are flying around a lever is pulled, and one lucky ball comes sliding down the chute for the winning number to be identified.

In your case the lever is estrogen, stimulating the Luteinizing Hormone (LH), which activates the *most ready* egg (ovum) to break out of its follicle capsule in the ovary. This egg slides down one of your two fallopian tubes and is possibly greeted by hundreds of handsome sperm, or perhaps none at all. This is *Ovulation*. I visualize this egg wearing a big, beautiful crown in Queen Bee fashion.

Studies are showing that conception happens when the *egg* does the choosing of the sperm, not the other way around.[24] I believe the sperm chosen is the one who wants to be with her the most, the one who swims the fastest and has the chemical makeup that pleases her. It could be that this is a microcosm and a symbolic representation for the way human romantic relationships work out best in the long run.

This is the MOMENT OF TRUTH in your cycle. If there are sperm waiting for your egg *or* if sperm can show up in the next 24

Express ~ Enchant ~ Enlighten

hours and a merging happens, it's called *conception*. The next step for this new couple-as-one (fertilized egg) is to attach and embed itself to the uterine lining, or nest, which can take seven to ten days. At this point, but not until then, a pregnancy is established. One could think of conception as "marriage" and the implantation as "pregnancy." In other words, if the newly "married" couple (fertilized egg) wants a child, it needs to walk a seven to ten day pilgrimage along the fallopian tube in preparation for this bundle of joy. This couple-as-one must experience the adventure of dividing into more and more cells, co-mingling as if in honeymoon lovemaking mode, until they turn into one big ball of cells. No life has begun developing yet—they are simply two wads of DNA involved in a merging and dividing preparation dance of potential. When the ball reaches its destination, it must touch and attach itself to the wall of the uterine lining in victory. They are *now* pregnant, and a new life will begin to grow within the ball of cells. The placenta will begin to develop on the outside of that ball of cells.[25]

Progesterone has also been released during this timeframe to make sure the uterine nest is fluffed, thickened, and ready to receive that fertile egg-ball of cells and to help keep it from miscarrying (naturally terminating/aborting).

Your Rhythm and The Pill:

If you are on birth control pills you most likely do not ovulate at all. The way most of them work is that they fake your body into thinking that it doesn't need to produce the hormones for Ovulation, so it doesn't. If you don't ovulate, you don't get pregnant. They *do* provide *synthetic* hormones to regulate your female body system in general. They also serve purposes beyond birth control such as controlling bleeding, easing bad cramps or hot flashes, and reducing acne. Discuss this with your doctor to discover the unique effects of birth control on you. Checking the website of the pharmaceutical company that makes your particular prescription might also give you more insight into the birth control you are using. Take the time to read the paper that comes with your pills.

Express ~ Enchant ~ Enlighten

If you don't ovulate, you will still peak at this point in your cycle, but not as much as if you were ovulating. Everything is subdued including your testosterone, which affects your sex drive, but your hormones *are* still fluctuating.

Ovulation darn near runs the world—it is the vortex into which all human sexuality is unconsciously drawn, stimulated by, and created for, so it seems a little crazy to me that most of us don't even know if we *do* or *do not* ovulate when we're on birth control pills! This is a major omission in women's health education. I am 100% in favor of birth control pills, but I want healthier ones developed. One researcher told me that the future of birth control resides with men. Since sperm are constantly manufactured, killing them with a systemic spermicide on a monthly basis wouldn't harm the endocrine system of the male (or the female he is with), nor have such drastic side effects as female birth control has. Keep in mind that having access to birth control for ourselves gives us more control over our bodies and therefore our lives. Having both options would be ideal.

For now, we just need to know how birth control pills affect us so that we can surf our own hormonal waves. We deserve to know what they do to our rhythm. We **NEED** to know in order to understand how they affect our health and well-being.

Fertility Awareness: If You Are NOT on The Pill

Ovulation happens over a roughly 24-hour period, but your Queen may hang out in the Fallopian Tube Lounge a little longer. It is important to talk with your practitioner about when you can have intercourse without using contraception if you don't want to get pregnant.

Reproduction Comparison: **Procreation Phase**

I have compared **Week 1, Fall** to the Birthing Phase of reproduction because it is the time when the uterus is shedding its contents. I've compared **Week 2, Winter** to the Courting Phase of reproduction because this is the week that our hormones are helping us attract a mate. I compare **Week 3, Spring** with the Procreation Phase of repro-

Express ~ Enchant ~ Enlighten

duction (marriage, intercourse, conception, and pregnancy) because Ovulation is the 24-hour period when an egg and sperm can merge.

Alert! Preventing Unwanted Pregnancies

Let's take a side journey for a few minutes to go over some *extremely important* sex education. No matter how knowledgeable you are, a little reminding could be the difference between making a clear decision and ending up with an unwanted pregnancy at a time when your brain and body are on sexual speed dial. This is done by making a solid plan now, *before* you get into the situation. My suggestion is to mentally go over how to stop the action if you are not getting birth control cooperation (or respect in general) from your partner. You may be particularly vulnerable if it has been a while since you've had sex or intimacy.

Facts and Timetable Reminders (all times are approximate)

We have established that the merging of an egg and sperm (conception) can only happen during a roughly 24-hour window of your cycle, when the egg is released from the ovary. HOWEVER, this is NOT the only time when having SEX is going to cause pregnancy—quite the CONTRARY. It's vital that you become a pro at understanding how this works.

- It takes about two hours for sperm to go from the vagina to the fallopian tube to wait for or meet the egg.

- Sperm sitting *at the entrance* of the vulva (the opening of the vagina) can make its way inside to begin this two-hour swim to the fallopian tube via fluids. This means the "pulling out" method of birth control is not at all reliable, no matter what *he* says. If he doesn't want to wear a condom and you don't want to try another type of contraception, then you must say no to him now, along with a reevaluation of your relationship. Do not allow semen (or juices, because they probably contain sperm)

Express ~ Enchant ~ Enlighten

near your opening even if you are not having intercourse. Those swimmers are quick and could help themselves into your portal.

∽ Semen ejaculations contain two to four million sperm. Only two to four HUNDRED are actually strong enough to make it to the fallopian tube to meet the egg.

∽ Even with these odds, a sperm and egg do not always connect.

∽ Reminder: Conception and pregnancy are NOT the same thing.

  • Conception is the merging of the sperm and the egg to create a fertilized egg, which happens in the fallopian tube. The fertilized egg then begins to travel to the uterus in order to attach itself to the uterine wall. This journey takes seven to ten days to complete the entire process. Yes, days!

∽ Pregnancy is established once the fertilized egg is firmly attached to the uterine wall, but not until then. Only 30 to 50 percent of fertilized eggs successfully attach naturally.[26]

∽ Hundreds of sperm can and will remain inside of you for up to seven days after having intercourse, waiting for the egg to make her appearance.[27]

→ If you have intercourse up to a week before Ovulation, some of the sperm will still be alive inside of you. They eventually die, with the exception that one might connect with the egg when she arrives.

This means, for instance, that if you have sex on Day 9 of your cycle, you will not necessarily conceive THAT day, but the sperm will live inside of you anywhere from three to seven days. If you ovulate on Day 15, then there is a very good chance that some of those same sperm have camped out long enough to greet your welcoming egg. If so, it's likely (but not guaranteed) that the egg will get fertilized and you will conceive.

So you would think, then, that up to seven days prior to Ovulation would be the ONLY time that you would be likely to become pregnant. **Wrong** again.

Express ~ Enchant ~ Enlighten

Because Ovulation is a moving target, it is very difficult to predict when you would be able to have sex without birth control and not get pregnant. If you end up ovulating on Day 11, for instance, it means you need to start using birth control properly beginning on Day 4, even if you're still bleeding. Because of the fluctuations of the actual Ovulation date, and sperm living inside of you for up to a week, you have a very wide window of opportunity for pregnancy.

What Can You Do?

If you believe you have had intercourse without birth control too close to Ovulation (within this week-long window), or you don't have a clue about your regular Ovulation time, you may be able to take the Morning After Pill (emergency contraception), which is a "super dose" of the Pill, to prevent Ovulation from happening. This is the way most birth control pills work—they prevent Ovulation from happening at all. If you don't ovulate you won't conceive. The sperm can be in there but if the egg is prevented from showing up, the party is over and everyone has to go home (be absorbed). So, taking the Morning After Pill any time up to seven days after intercourse may prevent you from ovulating and therefore prevent you from conceiving.

If you believe you have already ovulated but had sex before or during the 24-hour Ovulation period, taking the Morning After Pill *might* keep the *possibly* fertilized egg from attaching to the uterine wall. Remember, it takes seven to ten days for the fertilized egg to reach the uterine wall and attach itself. If a fertilized egg does not attach to the wall, there is no pregnancy. Pregnancy does not begin until it is firmly attached and a hormone called human chorionic gonadotropin (hCG) is released from the placenta to make the announcement.[28] Pregnancy tests rely on this hormone to identify pregnancy.

If pregnancy has already occurred, then the Morning After Pill will NOT harm it. The Morning After Pill is *not* an abortion pill.

It is worth saying that the Morning After Pill has been negatively and incorrectly characterized over the years as an abortion pill and

> Once the egg is either fertilized or "stood up on her date," ovulation is over.
>
> —Christiane Northrup, M.D.

Express ~ Enchant ~ Enlighten

restricted from being available to rape victims in hospital settings in many areas of the U.S. In many places it is not available at all, or it is not offered. In *most* cases it is available over the counter at pharmacies, for people aged 18 and over.[29] If the Morning After Pill is not in stock, any doctor who prescribes birth control should be able to replicate it with regular birth control pills. I'd like to note that the age restriction puts younger at-risk girls, who have no caring adult available to speak with, in a helpless, vulnerable, and precarious position. This can lead to a teen pregnancy that could have been avoided by preventing Ovulation, and therefore conception, from happening in the first place.

No Pregnancy

Let's get back to the process of Ovulation. If there are no sperm waiting, if there has been no prior intercourse when the egg slides down into the fallopian tube, she will wait approximately 24 hours for her date with destiny. If no one shows up, there is no conception and she'll be absorbed back into the uterine wall (probably feeling a little disgruntled in the process, or perhaps relieved!).

The hormone progesterone is a little like a nanny. It is there to ensure the safety of the fertilized egg and keep her happy in the uterine nest. It will be present for seven to ten days, waiting for a fertilized egg to show up. If there is a no-show, the nurturing progesterone is no longer needed and begins to rapidly leave the system, until it comes back again next month.

Your hormones will begin the process of dismantling the uterine nest in the same way that the full light of the Moon now begins to lessen, or wane. This deconstruction process of the uterine nest will continue until it is shed in the form of blood in **Week 1, Fall**.

Characteristics
Week 3, Spring

Reminder: The 4s4w strategy, or system, was created for the sole purpose of putting the feminine cycle into perspective in order to relate our experiences to its week-to-week and day-to-day changes and remembering how they go without too much effort.

Each woman is different and ultimately must identify and adjust her own rhythm, but the hormonal influences of each phase tend to have the general characteristics of the seasons. The 4s4w system attempts to add meaning to these characteristics.

The Feminine Cycle (Days 15–21)

Because 4s4w identifies Ovulation as a marker day, or point of reference, **Week 3, Spring** is designed to *begin* with Ovulation in the same way that **Week 1, Fall** begins with the first day of your Period, the other marker day.

Your week begins with Ovulation, so your most outgoing personality and libido are already at their peak. Take advantage of it while also doing your best to be mindful of the long-term consequences of your sexual decisions. This party only lasts about 24 hours, but the effects can last a lifetime. You've already been experiencing a sexual euphoria leading up to this point in **Week 2, Winter**, and you have been using it to fuel your projects or to make positive progress in your relationships. You have been using your vast energy to get things done, so you can now kick back and enjoy the party.

Symbolically, Ovulation represents your highest self and everything that you are. What can happen biologically in this tiny window of time is what rules your female body. This is something to face instead of wishing it would go away, or disavowing it altogether. This ONE day out of 28 is the Queen Bee Day, while the other 27 days are the worker bees who support it.

For this reason it is vital for your health and your future planning

Express ~ Enchant ~ Enlighten

to learn and understand as much as you can about this day that kicks off **Week 3, Spring**. It is the shining star, the main character of our lives, whether we admit it or not.

Once Ovulation happens, your sex drive will begin to back off but your energy will most likely remain steady. As you rapidly enter the phase of Enlightened Wisdom, the Wise Woman, and World Leader, you'll continue to express yourself outwardly. Spring carries on and only the glory wanes as you transition into **Week 4, Summer**, the week of *Emoping* (the Emotional Period) and the Fire Walk, the time we begin to eliminate the things in our lives that no longer serve us.

How the *Characteristics* of Spring, the Moon, and the Feminine Cycle Relate

Days and Nights: We enter our lightest days of the year at the Vernal Equinox, brightening all the more as we reach for the Summer Solstice in June. Ready to extend the inner warmth of our hearts in Winter to the outer world of Spring, we find ourselves eager to break out of our own cocoons to expose our glorious butterflies. Light brightens our spirits and personalities and fuels the bursting forth of new growth. Similarly, the ovum bursts out of its shell to present itself to new possibilities.

Spring Fever: Spring is a very exciting time. We catch Spring fever in one way or another the moment we feel the transition from Winter, whether it is preparing our gardens, riding our bikes, hauling kids around for Little League, or getting together with friends. We *go* outside. We like to *be* outside. We feel *alive* outside. Outside! We leave the confines of our homes and greet our neighbors as we collect our mail, fix sprinklers, and watch the kids play. The Sun begins to warm our bones and that feels good. The warmer days and coldish nights are a sexy pair, encouraging the same from us. Inner urges prompt and nudge us to get out there and commingle. Warmer temperatures and gentle breezes stimulate our senses.

Our hormones push us to become the extroverted versions of ourselves during this week. As in Spring, when we venture out to

Express ~ Enchant ~ Enlighten

socialize, this is the week in our cycle when we bring our personalities all the way forward for everyone to see and experience. We are extroverted socially and we are extroverted sexually. We glisten and tease.

Spring Cleaning: Spring is also the time when we open up windows for fresh air and clean out drawers and cabinets. We hold garage sales and take stuff to the Goodwill. We clear our gardens of any extra Fall and Winter debris and turn the soil, creating a new seed bed for the upcoming crops. Spring is a time when many people fast or do other types of internal body cleansing or detoxification. Often this is combined with a new workout routine and nutritional plan. So much of the feminine cycle seems to be about cleaning out the old to prepare for the new.

Purification: Purification takes the concept of Spring cleaning into the mind and soul. Spring represents purification, with snow

melting into fresh rushing rivers, cleansing the Earth of stagnation. Spring represents rebirth. The old self dies then comes to life renewed, ridding the mind of negative thoughts, fears, or anger, and creating room for transformation through confidence, beauty, and love; in religious terms, shedding sin to receive salvation.

Like the Spring cleaning of our homes, it is the time we decide to Spring clean our conscious minds and allow ourselves to bring subconscious behaviors to the surface. Feeling pure in our essence is attractive and readies us for new beginnings. Ovulation is sacred. It allows us to experience the purity of Nature. We are able to see the purity of our Authentic Female and allow only the right partner to our personal party.

This purification process continues throughout the week, after

Express ~ Enchant ~ Enlighten

Ovulation, while we sit on our glorious spiritual thrones. As Wise Women, we evaluate the party that has happened with acute clarity and wisdom, tuning in to the Divine to understand our day-to-day selves.

Innocence: There is no other season that represents innocence the way Spring does. Spring is the time of birth for many baby animals. Babies are vulnerable and so are we, every single time we present something new to the world, no matter how experienced we are in life.

Virginity is an emotional, symbolic experience and not exclusive to the physical "never had sex" body. Rather, it is a sense of inexperience, unsureness, naiveté, risk, and a purity that goes with doing something, *anything*, for the first time.

Week 3, Spring is the time we are encouraged to express ourselves fully, like the Full Moon. The ovum bursts out of its shell to present itself to the waiting sperm in hopes of making a connection, just as we are encouraged to burst out of our shells to present *our* selves to the world in hopes of making a connection. When we put ourselves out there—expressing a new idea, taking a risk, exposing who we really are, what we've been working on, or sharing our bodies with another (whether it is the first time or the hundredth)—it is a new dawn, a new day to feel the love of something new *and* feel the fear of rejection. Every month, during this **Week 3, Spring**, we have a greater-than-usual chance to experience innocence, to be reborn, to start over again, to be beautiful and renewed.

Rain: "April showers bring May flowers," as the saying goes. Our juices are wet, mucus-like, and sticky in order to help the sperm body surf its way to the fallopian tube and out of harm's way of the acidic opening at the vulva. Spring is generally the wettest time of the year and Ovulation is the wettest time of our cycle.

Romance and Flowers: Flowers are a part of the awakening sexual experience. Flowers are the most common expression of love to others, be it family, friend, or romantic interest. Their visual beauty, along with their lovely fragrance, brings peace and harmony to the heart. Flowers are given to another to please, to soothe, or as a peace offering. Red roses are a token of love, a request to be in or stay in

Express ~ Enchant ~ Enlighten

partnership. Ovulation is the greatest expression of this intention, an internal flower coming forth.

Flowers raise the sensory vibration of environments and humans by making any room or yard feel and look spectacular and sophisticated. From our fertile land, Ovulation takes us to the *spiritual place of creation*. Petaled flowers are the symbols of our most personal and private doorways, with lotus flowers, specifically, being a symbol of enlightenment.

Pollination: Spring is the time when we imagine the birds and the bees pollinating fertile flowers, flying from one to another, spreading pollen. From this specialized activity more flowers are assured for the future. Ovulation is the time the male seed, in the form of sperm, penetrates the ovum in order to fertilize it, after the seed enters our flower-like temple.

Memories: *Scent*-uality and *Sense*-uality: Your memories of Spring are unique to you. My memories of Spring are mostly aromatic, although *all* of my *senses* do come to life in the Spring. Aromatherapy teaches us that our sense of smell touches our most primal level of survival instincts by "smelling danger" or activating our pleasure zones. The ability to evoke sensual memories is possibly olfaction's grandest gift. Smelling something that you've smelled before will evoke a memory, taking you straight to a particular place and time. Spring arouses us because there are so many aromas that smell like being in love, smells that perhaps remind you of places where you dated, such as baseball games, mountain lakes where you rode bikes, a bed of spicy carnations where you first kissed, or the strawberry patch where you fed your boyfriend a freshly plucked strawberry. Maybe it is the effervescent air, ocean breeze, or warm afternoon that will unearth your passion.

For many people Spring is *a sensual* time. We have energy in Spring because our *senses* have been renewed, brought to life. Dewey mornings invite us to take a deep breath and inhale the rich aromas of the plants, flowers, and trees. Fertile soil reminds us that the Earth's body, as well as our own, is ripe for planting.

Express ~ Enchant ~ Enlighten

> **Moisture. Greenery. Flowers. Aromas. Primal sensuality. Sexuality. Spirituality.** Nature rules us, awakening us to the highest spiritual attunement. Spring rain and morning mist invigorate and awaken our *senses*. Night jasmine arouses our yearnings. Spring is the *sensual* time of the year, and the third week is the sensual phase of our cycle.

Symbolic Transitions & Influences
Week 3, Spring

Since **Week 3, Spring** is part of a cycle in motion, the first day of the week is different from the last day of the week. Our physical bodies *and* our Mind Moods change daily.

Influences on the Body, Mind, and Soul: The Big Os

Mind Moods and ARCHETYPES

Day 15: The Big O

- At One with the Universe: THE GODDESS
- Ovulation: The Party
- Obsession
- Own it
- Oprah
- The Orb: Pure Clarity
- The Opposite Effect: Total Eclipse

Express ~ Enchant ~ Enlighten

Days 16–21: Enlightened Wisdom

- ⟿ Wise Woman
- ⟿ Close to the Source
- ⟿ World Leader: Global Mother and Peace Ambassador
- ⟿ Calm clarity
- ⟿ Lasting impression
- ⟿ Physical symptoms
- ⟿ Expectations
- ⟿ Sexpectations
- ⟿ Feeling appreciated

In the same way that **Week 1, Fall** begins on the first day of the Period, **Week 3, Spring** begins with Ovulation day. Ovulation can be seen symbolically as the peak of the cycle with much happening, so I am combining body, mind, and soul influences in **Week 3, Spring**. I will talk about this week in two parts: the first day, Ovulation, and the rest of the week, Enlightened Wisdom.

The Big O

At One With the Universe: THE GODDESS

Our physicality draws our minds to sex, and sexual thoughts encourage our bodies to feel the heightened sensations that run through our veins. Yet there is a much bigger scene going on here besides sexuality. This is a vibrational high that connects the lowest chakra at the base of the spine, the

Express ~ Enchant ~ Enlighten

energy point for survival, to the highest chakra at the top of the head, the energy point for spiritual awakening. It connects "Oh My God!" to "Om, Shanti."

> Om is the sound of the Universe in Sanskrit (transmuted to "Amen" in Christianity); *shanti* means peace, and can be interpreted as "I am a peaceful soul," or "I am bliss." Many believe these are the sweetest words in the Universe.

I am at One with the Universe when I am Ovulating. I am the Goddess who rules all.

Ovulation: The Party

Think of Ovulation as a party in the same way as throwing a reunion, a wedding, or having friends over for dinner. You prepare for this event well in advance. Excitement, tension, and a sense of urgency build just prior to the day. How will it go? How will you be received? How well do you know your guests?

Ovulation is the party your body (and booty) has been preparing for during the previous week. It is the Top of the Mountain, the Destination, the Orgasm of your female cycle. It is the Moment of Truth: the truth about your fertility, your connection, your communication, but mainly the truth about knowing yourself and how well you are expressing your truth and gifts to the world.

The goal of Ovulation, and therefore your entire cycle, *and* hence your entire life, is to get in tune with the purity of YOU: your thoughts, your words, your actions, your values, your self-worth, your principles, your boundaries, the gifts you were born with, and the talents you've developed. It is vital to align these things for your optimal life experience. It is vital to align these things to attract the right partner for yourself as well.

If you find yourself in an unhappy relationship, think about how you got into the relationship to begin with. Was it purely physical

Express ~ Enchant ~ Enlighten

attraction? Did he fit a need or many needs? Did *he* go after *you* and that made you feel special, wanted, and needed, but now you are finding you don't have much in common? Did *you* go after *him* and now find him to be a reluctant partner?

All of these are very common ways to end up in a *stuck* relationship. Perhaps you aren't clear about your true values, self-worth, and boundaries. If this is the case, you are not bringing your true self into your relationship.

We continue to discover our true selves throughout our lifetimes. Getting as clear as possible, as soon as possible, about who you really are is going to result in the best outcome in all of your relationships: romantic, family, friends, and business endeavors.

Ovulation represents the very best of you—your authentic self who lives honestly, confidently, wisely, and compassionately. You may just find that you are already there. Now maintain it.

> To "want" and to be ambitious and to want to be successful is not enough. That's just desire. To know what you want, to understand . . . why you're doing it, to dedicate every breath in your body, to achieve . . . If you feel that you have something to give, if you feel that your particular talent is worth developing, is worth caring for, then there's nothing you can't achieve.
>
> —Kevin Spacey

For starters, create or be a part of projects that complement and align with your values and principles, as well as your highest hopes and dreams for yourself and the world. In romantic relationships, it is crucial to align yourself with a partner who is supportive of your dreams and talents and who cares about your well-being. It is important that you, in turn, are supportive and care about *his* dreams and talents as well. You must truly *like* this person and he must truly *like* you. Sometimes it is easier to love a person than to actually *like* him or her. Be sure the groups you join or people you spend time with honor the standards you value. The more *pure* you are in your clarity

Express ~ Enchant ~ Enlighten

about your standards and expectations, the more you will attract the life you desire.

When it comes to your sexuality it is vital to make healthy decisions about *who* you are doing *what* with. Keep your standards at their highest and you will attract the best. When in a state of solitude or loneliness, be careful not to say "yes" to just anyone. Have patience and faith to get rewarded with a better union.

Ovulation is about being "high" in the most positive sense, standing your tallest. It is the place where your standards, sexuality, spiritual connection, clear boundaries, and self-esteem are at their highest. Take a look at them. Are they where you would like them to be?

> Each time you remember the truth of who you are, you bring more light into the world.
>
> —Gaelyn Larrick

Obsession

Ovulation represents the height of your sexuality because this is the day your egg breaks out of your ovary and beckons a sperm to come and greet her. On this day, and for many days before, you'll most likely feel naturally intoxicated with amped energy and attraction.

This natural intoxication is a mind and body obsession. It can be very hard to concentrate because the mind is so aware of the body's sexual sensations and you will most likely find your thoughts wandering off to fantasy land. This is a very good time to stand in your man's shoes. Is this how he feels on a daily basis?

Own It

Ovulation is the time in my cycle when I can literally walk into a place and feel like I own the joint. My energy feels limitless. Imagine being Glinda the Good Witch floating in on her big pink bubble. It's like that. She looks calm, serene, wise, beautiful, and in charge in a good way. Everyone is drawn to her.

This is you on Ovulation.

The first time I felt this, it took me completely off guard—I felt out-of-body. Later I realized the sensation matched my cycle. All I had to do was to look at my calendar and sure enough, I was ovulating. Nowadays I know what day I'm on and just go with it.

Glinda the Good Witch represents pure and infinite female power. Nobody, and I mean nobody, over the rainbow is more powerful than she is. She is the closest thing to God they have, especially once everyone discovers the Great and Powerful Wizard of Oz is just a man with smoke and mirrors. She *is* quintessential Beauty and Brains, Goddess, Wise Woman, and World Leader. She's got unshakable confidence and a wand that can wipe out evil *and* wake people up from their unconsciousness. More importantly, she's got the drop-dead party dress, along with the biggest and best crown one could ever hope for. She's kind and sweet, but knows exactly where her boundaries are and doesn't allow anyone to cross them. "You have no power here!" she pleasantly but firmly informs the Wicked Witch of the West. "Go home before someone drops a house on you!" No negative presences in her beautiful land.

That huge bubble of hers is Ovulation in motion, the egg that just came popping out of its cocoon, the Full Moon in all its glory, the giant womb representing the power of our fertile flowing spirits. Spring is here. Pure clarity about what you want and who you are is the most powerful type of human attraction there is.

Oprah

As far as I'm concerned, there is no woman on the planet who exudes the essence of Ovulation and the Sacred Feminine more than Oprah. She is the epitome of full expression, connection, compassion, transformation, beauty, wisdom, big vision, and world leadership. It is no coincidence that her magazine is called "O."

She is Glinda, the Authentic Female, and Womb Wisdom (that cool, dark, transformational, unconditional love, and home to all) combined, working for the good of all and doing her best to help us discover our own healthy authenticity in all of her and our imperfections. With a television network and all the trimmings to relay her messages, she went from having less than nothing to being perhaps the most powerful woman in the world. Yet she is humble and real.

Express ~ Enchant ~ Enlighten

With Sacred Feminine, right brain, big picture vision, and Sacred Masculine, left brain focus, she continues to share her own personal struggles while sharing her gifts from the soul. She asks us to reach into the depths of our beings to take a look and wipe out the unhealthy in order to heal our wounded hearts and present our gifts to the world.

The Orb: Operating with Clarity

The Orb is a term I use in business to identify the vision, values, principles, and dreams of an operation. Once clarified, all decisions are made with this focus in mind. Although it is not magic, I picture it looking like a crystal ball. Getting clearer in areas we didn't know we were fuzzy in *does* help us to see the future. When we know where we are it is easier to make quick decisions to support where we're going.

> You could write a song about some kind of emotional problem you are having, but it would not be a good song, in my eyes, until it went through a period of sensitivity to a moment of clarity. Without that moment of clarity to contribute to the song, it's just complaining. —Joni Mitchell

Begin finding this new clarity by jotting down your values, principles, goals, boundaries, and highest hopes and dreams for yourself, as well as the things you are drawn to. Be more and more specific as you get into this exercise.

In his book, **Shiny Objects Marketing,** marketing master David LaBonte talks about finding "the shiny object" in your product or business that you're trying to promote, because people will be attracted to it without even knowing why. The same goes for *you*. Pure clarity is a beautiful shiny object and will literally change how you look, bringing out your sparkle and glow. When you clear away the cloudy layers of *who you are not*, bringing forth your beautiful diamond self, your personality will transform into a calmer, clearer, happier, and sexier version of you. Your charm becomes contagious and charismatic, just like springtime.

Express ~ Enchant ~ Enlighten

The Opposite Effect: Total Eclipse

Many women, though, feel worse on this day than on any other day in their cycle, experiencing irritation and depression.

This could be due to the estrogen peak that triggers Ovulation a day or two before and then drops suddenly. As a migraine-prone person, I notice that the estrogen peak can bring on a headache. I can avoid this by being mindful of what day I'm on and make sure I'm eating cleanly, exercising, and resting properly to counter this effect.

If you are on birth control pills, you are most likely not ovulating at all, which means your estrogen and testosterone levels are lower than they would be naturally. It could be that your female body, hard-wired for Ovulation, is going through the motions anyway, yet feeling frustrated by the lack of excitement reached. Talk to your doctor. Find out what your hormones are doing.

If it's not a physical thing from birth control pills or a hormonal imbalance, a subconscious and symbolic reason for this "down" could be that the party started and you aren't ready. Maybe the man of your dreams hasn't entered your life, or maybe you are feeling a lack of direction and focus. If you haven't found the success in life you hoped for, or the great relationship you crave, perhaps this day wells up that frustration inside you, painful and unsettling.

If you're not feeling a high at this point in your cycle, it's important to get a handle on why that is. Knowing the reason will help you to find resolution more quickly, or at least keep you from bottoming out.

Express ~ Enchant ~ Enlighten

Ovulation Challenge #1: The general euphoric intoxication of Ovulation can make a mess of things if you haven't gotten pure about your clarity beforehand. It can also be greatly diminished if alcohol or other substances are blocking your core feminine power and beauty. When you are partying hard, you are trading in your highest, most fabulous high for a low-level high that has negative side-effects. The natural high attracts; the low-level high turns people off.

If, over a few months, you've gotten clearer about your values and desires, and done your best to identify and clean up any destructive habits, then this confidence that Ovulation provides can put you on a fast track to your dreams.

Ovulation Challenge #2: Sexual intoxication is the name of the game at the beginning of this week. This is great if you already have a devoted partner and your lusty affection leans in his direction. But I'm here to tell you that you need to watch out and be attentive about with whom you are choosing to share your essence and sacred vessel. Many a friend has found herself saying "yes" when she should be saying "no." It's very easy to *not* make particularly great decisions about men during this time.

More and more studies are showing that, around Ovulation time, women's brains light up in areas associated with rewards (which could include such things as sex, drugs, and alcohol) more than the areas associated with inhibition and control. This heightened sensitivity around Ovulation suggests that women can be more vulnerable to risky behavior at this time in their cycles.[30]

You walk a tightrope here. You want to attract the right sweetie, not the wrong one. This is where the purity of your

Express ~ Enchant ~ Enlighten

clarity comes in. When you begin to get clearer and clearer about your values, principles, and self-worth, you'll get better and better at eliminating the men who are unhealthy for you, no matter how hot! And you'll get better and better at attracting the right ones.

Ovulation Challenge #3: If you're not on The Pill, you must be disciplined and vigilant about using other types of birth control correctly, even if your man is not. If he's not, my suggestion is to ask yourself whether this is someone who actually looks out for your best interests and the best interests of the relationship. If you don't want to get pregnant, then you must be strong in this regard.

Ovulation Challenge #4: If you are a person who has sex regularly at all phases of your cycle, then you're probably wondering what the big deal is here about Ovulation. Perhaps, for you, sex at this phase is no different from any other time. What I'm saying is that your libido *should* be heightened here and sex should be more exciting. Have you gotten too routine about things? Look for ways to spice things up, or ask yourself if you're being satisfied.

Ovulation Challenge #5: If you are not in a relationship and would like to be, or are in an unhappy relationship, then watch out for being cranky, or even depressed, during this time. You may feel a jealous fury if your man is not connecting with you and only you. Ovulation represents the purest form of connection—the most sacred of connections—so if his sexual focus is aimed at other women, then it is time to have a serious conversation about your relationship to make sure you're both on the same page.

Express ~ Enchant ~ Enlighten

Ovulation Challenge #6: If you find yourself feeling blue and weepy for any reason, my suggestion is to exercise—hard! The endorphins will help your mindset. Join up with people and projects in alignment with your intended direction. Of course, if this low feeling persists, seek help from a trusted professional.

Ovulation Challenge #7: Perhaps you are ready to have a baby but the man of your dreams, or even the man for the job, has not yet entered the picture. Perhaps you have the man, but fertility is a challenge. You may be experiencing a reverse *Empty Nest Syndrome*. Whatever the circumstances, do your best to be kind to yourself. Join a group of like-minded women or seek help from a trusted professional if you need an ear and advice.

Ovulation Challenge #8: Just as obsession about sex can consume your thoughts, obsession about a break-up, people at work, or any other sort of unhappy scenario can consume your mind and not go away. I call this *obsession-in-retrograde*. This is the type of obsession that won't let your mind alone even though you wish it would. You thought you were over your guy, only to find that your thoughts about him won't go away. You may be thinking back on incidences that led to a breakup, or you may be obsessing over what he is doing and with whom he is doing it.

It is natural for us to want a partner at this juncture of our cycle, so it seems likely that this phase triggers our deepest longings to get our relationship piece right.

Express ~ Enchant ~ Enlighten

The first day of **Week 3, Spring** is Ovulation. The rest of **Week 3, Spring** moves into what Christiane Northrup, M.D., calls "the reflection phase." The reflection phase continues throughout the entire second half of your cycle. The Full Moon begins to wane, setting out on its journey to darken, to go inward again, and so do you.

Shining a Light on it All— Enlightened Wisdom

WISE WOMAN

Basking in the glow of Ovulation, your *Enlightened Wise Woman* steps in to look over all that has happened in your cycle so far. Shining the brightest of light on your circumstances and choices, this *enlightened* phase brings new opportunity for you to make real change where it is needed in your world—personally and globally. It is time for speaking out contemplatively, responsibly, and diplomatically, and communicating with your romantic partner and other important people in your life.

Standing in the luminous just-past-Full Moon, shining its beacon on your cycle thus far, your Wise Woman—one of the many archetypes of your Authentic Female—is able to look back and evaluate the validity of your expectations and express your thoughts from an elevated, bigger-picture, solid, and compassionate point of view. This is where our Femi-

Express ~ Enchant ~ Enlighten

nine and Masculine merge—our brain hemispheres operating from a place of balance. If you don't tune in to yourself here, you are losing out on your most valuable asset—the highest vibration of *you*.

Merging with Source

Ancient sexual teachings suggest that orgasm is the closest thing to reaching God if two people synchronize their breathing and practice heightened connection. Ovulation is the peak, the crest, and the magnetic force around which our sexual Universe revolves. Ovulation is the orgasm of the female cycle. It is the genesis of conception, the merging of a sperm and an egg. One doesn't get that close to Source and not be struck by the "enlightenment rod."

As the human *source* of creation, we merge with the *Source of All* at Ovulation, giving us the opportunity for epiphany month after month. Our personal Sacred Feminine whispers words of wisdom while waiting patiently to surface. Lift the fog! Wake *Her* completely! Imagine how the world would benefit if we teach our young women to nurture and understand this gift early on in order to tap in to a more conscious way of being and living!

WORLD LEADER: Global Mother and Peace Ambassador

Progesterone, the calming and nurturing hormone, now starts to rise, taking over where estrogen left off, making life easier by helping us to feel centered and clear. Being free from last week's excitement of creating and attracting, there is room to breathe and expand. This clarity brings me great solace and awareness beyond my everyday intelligence. I'm in the mood to take care of things now—to nurture myself by taking charge of my life, nurture my family by getting organized, nurture the environment by seeing the connectedness of all, and nurturing my world community's health and well-being by participating in its peace and justice process. Whether you have children or not, this nurturing, mothering nature, along with the talent to peacefully negotiate, is an instinct we can all tap in to at this part of our cycle— for our families and our world.

Express ~ Enchant ~ Enlighten

This particular window in your female recycling system shows that you are meant to be a World Leader. Whether you are standing tall at the highest elevation, sexually, productively, and spiritually satiated, or disappointed because you are *not*, your varied *experience* has given you the gift of knowing that you are capable of accomplishing anything, or the gift of knowing how to take a look at why you are not. Free of the distraction and intoxication of Ovulation, you are at the pinnacle of your woman-

hood—*your* Authentic Female, should you choose to recognize her. She is radiant, clear, and energetically calm.

Your Wise Woman muse and World Leader work together to constantly remind you that learning and refining is an ongoing process, and that the only perfection that actually exists is the undulating journey *itself*—trial and error, learning from our mistakes, and making forward motion from love, not fear. Harsh judgment of others has no place in this world of taking a look at our own stuff. However, our rhythmic Mind Moods allow for a unique perspective on where the healthy flow patterns in our world systems lie, where the waters are dammed up, and how they might be fixed. The Authentic Female inside each of us knows it is Her responsibility to participate in the positive shaping and molding of our society, just as it is our responsibility to participate in the positive shaping and molding of our children, families, and communities. It only makes sense that Source put your most sharply tuned mothering instinct into your rhythm at this juncture.

Express ~ Enchant ~ Enlighten

Lasting Impression

During the days following Ovulation you have come down off of your high, yet you still have energy and heightened awareness. You may find yourself naturally taking a break from sex, even if you are not aware that you have ovulated. Take note of this sign. This little break may give you an indication that you did indeed ovulate. Give yourself time to catch your breath after the fun frenzy of your heightened activity.

If Ovulation is the Moment of Truth, then the following days are the proof of the pudding. The days following the Ovulation party will leave lasting impressions you'll carry with you into **Summer, Week 4**, providing you with the wisdom to make the right adjustments.

So…check in. The party is over. How do you feel after trying something new during sex, or presenting a project to the world? Was it good stuff or not quite right? Do you feel weird or uncomfortable? Did new, improved connections develop? Are things going in the right direction? Did you honor your self-worth and boundaries?

Hopefully, a sense of satisfaction lingers as you sit back and admire your garden of achievements. Seeds of yourself that you had planted in the world and exchanged in your relationship have been given a chance to grow. Are the sprouts that are coming out of the ground what you expected? Do they look like what you intended?

If the results fall short, then you'll need to take a look at the kinds of expectations you've been holding. Are you and your significant other living up to your expectations? Are you hitting the mark regarding where you thought you would be at this point in your life?

Physical Signs

This is a fabulous time to begin taking a look at the symbolism of how much you go for it and how often you play it safe. When you get into the purity of being clear—understanding the source of your thoughts and actions, along with your values and boundaries—you will know you possess the power to create the life you desire.

Express ~ Enchant ~ Enlighten

It is particularly important to note how your body feels during this Spring Week. Are you relaxed and feeling good? Hooray, you're getting better at knowing yourself! The more you know yourself, the more others will understand where you are coming from and the cleaner your relationships with family and friends will be.

If your gut is uptight just after mid-cycle, it's time for an overall check-in with yourself. Remember, Ovulation can actually be about sex, or it can *represent* a passion in your life, manifested or not.

Did you succumb to the brain intoxication that had you saying yes when you should have said no? Did you forget to relax and have fun at your party (heightened sex drive, or whatever passionate project you're doing this month)? Perhaps you said no when you should have said yes, and now your guy is getting bored with you for not playing and having fun, or the people involved in your projects don't believe you are as interested as they are. Do you say things that you don't really feel deep down inside just so you'll fit in? Do you say things you don't really mean because you don't want to make waves? Are you frustrated with those around you for not doing what they agreed to do, or with your guy, for not playing the way you'd like *him* to play? Are you articulating your needs well, or do you expect everyone to read your mind? Are you secretly wishing your sex life was different?

After Ovulation it's not unusual to experience feelings of disappointment or regret, perhaps even a hint of anger, not quite knowing why you're feeling edgy. During this part of your cycle you might be questioning yourself about your judgment or your life in general.

Expectations

It is natural to evaluate all the intimate interactions with your partner or your projects, your sense of vulnerability, what went well, and what needs to improve. Once you get good at this portion of the process, you'll realize that you indeed carry expectations. Some were fulfilled, others were not. These expectations are big and run deep, yet you are likely unaware of them. They are the type of expectations that affect

Express ~ Enchant ~ Enlighten

your core being—your femininity, your self-esteem, and your value to the world—the kind of stuff that leaves us feeling naked and exposed when not fulfilled.

This Spring Week, this symbolic Full Moon time, is the perfect chance to shine a light on your deepest expectations, hopes, and dreams. You'll need to be open to seeing them, asking yourself if they are reasonable and if you are making the right choices to manifest them.

Defensiveness is a key indicator of expectations. When things aren't right, and you find yourself blaming your partner or blaming your workplace, it's time to evaluate. What is yours to own in this disconnect? Your expectations may be valid if your partner is disappointing you after you have made certain agreements. Maybe you failed to inform him and others of your plans or standards. Perhaps you didn't plan for the party very well and are looking for someone else to blame. Whatever the reasons, the most important thing is to *feel*, investigate, and identify. If you can identify what is yours, and acknowledge your responsibility in the disconnection, you might actually be able to laugh about it, or at least make a sincere apology, and resolve to pay attention to it next month. You might also discover that this reveals a door that opens into a broader issue for you or your loved ones.

Sexpectations

Sex and romance can provide some of the most wonderful experiences in your life. They can also create some of the most disappointing times, even leading to loneliness, despair, and regret.

What is it that you truly want with respect to sex and romance? Everyone has high hopes and dreams. Have they turned into expectations that your partner doesn't even know about or agree with? Do you have expectations for a future partner that are too ideal for any man to match? Do you have sexual fantasies that are not realized because you are afraid to voice them? I call all of these "sexpectations."

Post-Ovulation is the time to recognize these sexpectations in or-

Express ~ Enchant ~ Enlighten

der to own your stuff. It's time to be realistic about what is attainable and what isn't. Getting very clear about your sexpectations is key to communicating your desires with your partner or future partner. It is key to getting a handle on disappointment and minimizing frustration.

Feeling Appreciated

I believe that every month we revisit and reevaluate how much our man appreciates us. The truth is that he must court us throughout the month, and every day during **Week 2, Winter**, to keep the relationship truly alive. We also revisit and reevaluate how much our work, or children, or extended family, appreciates us, as well. We evaluate how much time we are putting into them all and whether we are feeling depleted or fulfilled.

Competitive Spirit: Transitioning to Week 4, Summer

Your Enlightened Wise Woman puts on her running shoes and ventures energetically into **Week 4, Summer**, the days before the Period. Symbolically these are the hottest, most uncomfortable days of the cycle. The waning moonlight narrows into a spotlight, turning itself inward to sharpen its focus on the one thing that matters most: your heart's desire.

Adjusting the Days of This Week

Do you need to adjust your **Week 3, Spring** by moving it up a few days earlier in the cycle? After a few rounds of tracking and observing, you'll begin to see where you ovulate and where the transitions are. You may find that **Week 1, Fall** can be shortened, as can **Week 2, Winter**. It's something you can discuss with your health practitioner at your next exam.

Express ~ Enchant ~ Enlighten

To-Do List
Week 3, Spring

Activities

- Upon awakening, take a couple of minutes to
  - Figure out what cycle day you are on
  - Acknowledge what is basically happening with your hormones
  - Set an intention for the day regarding your health and well-being
- Have fun, dress well, and sizzle.
- Let go of the organizing and let the party happen.
- If Ovulation time is about sex, try some new things; initiate and receive; allow yourself to go to greater heights; allow your body and your spirit to expand, to open.
- If Ovulation represents a concept, project, or event you are trying to initiate or conceive, then let it come to fruition or step back and congratulate yourself for what you've done up to this point; if it's not quite ready yet, visualize the project finished and revel in it.
- After Ovulation, take time to sit on your throne and contemplate.

Food

- Try some sexy foods; take a look at *4s4w's Food for a Female Planet* for aphrodisiac food ideas
- "Spring Cleaning" begins after Ovulation; reduce or eliminate sugars and fatty foods in order to prepare and create an inflammation-free zone for **Week 4, Summer**.

Express ~ Enchant ~ Enlighten

Sleep

- Ovulation: A regular sleep pattern is always recommended, but this phase lets you get by with less sleep.

- Post-Ovulation: Time to get disciplined about a regular and full sleep pattern; kick it into gear now so that you feel your healthiest and most rested for **Summer, Week 4**.

Exercise

You should definitely be moving a lot at this phase, through exercise, or sex, or both. Exercising during this week will help to keep your mind balanced as well, helping you to make better decisions throughout the intoxicating time before and during Ovulation. It will also help you to burn off sexual energy if you're not sexually active.

Relationships

This is the time to focus on your sexual relationship or presenting your projects and then evaluating how it's going. Although family and friends are not the highlight of your focus this week, your energy is good for multi-tasking and incorporating them into your flow.

As the Moment of Truth for your romantic relationship, are you two connected?

Sex

Ovulation: **Spring** is the week that you reap all the benefits of the great communication you did in **Week 2, Winter**. After getting warmed up with various forms of foreplay (great talks, fun, affection, and tender lovemaking), your meter is running hot. Since Ovulation is, in a sense, the orgasm of your cycle, the fullest Moon, you are peaking now. As long as you have contraception under control when you do not want to conceive, and if you are with the right partner for you, then allow yourself to go for it—every sense is super-heightened, especially the nipples. They might be highly sensitive in a good and tough way. They can take a lot and want a lot. Forget making

Express ~ Enchant ~ Enlighten

slow love—this is the time to get hot and heavy, down and dirty. Spring is rainy season and you are wet and well-lubricated, so clear your schedule, eat in, and take total advantage of this time.

If you don't have a partner, there is no need to deprive yourself of sex. Get a vibrator and get to know yourself. These days most sex stores are for men *and* women. Besides, learning to please yourself, manually or with a toy, is an important aspect of knowing what you actually like. This will help your confidence tremendously when the right partner comes along.

Post-Ovulation: You may not be on the high that you have been, but if you are happy with how the first part of the week went, and you're both into it, then certainly keep it going. The more sex, the better, between couples who are mutually committed to developing a healthy relationship.

Personal Inquiry
Week 3, Spring

How do you feel physically this week?

Did your *Mind Moods* change throughout the week?

In what ways are you expressing your sexuality?

Are you expressing it with sex or with projects?

How do you feel after Ovulation?

Have you noticed any expectations or sexpectations?

What has your cycle looked like so far?

Are you beginning to understand it?

Express ~ Enchant ~ Enlighten

Ovulation

The egg drops with so much sparkle
Everyone will be drawn in
Innocent yet sexual
Here where new life may begin

You have prepared to say your truth
Speaking wisely, fearless ring
Now the others see you blossom
Like a flower in the Spring

The Full Moon makes us howl
   with glee
Pregnant in its sacred light
The sky is beautiful and vast
Behold! Passion and love unite.

—Sylvia Seroussi Chatroux, M.D.
Poetica Press

Express ~ Enchant ~ Enlighten

The ManGuide

Week 3, Spring

"King"

This week is one of the great rewards, for both you and your sweetheart, of following the 4s4w system. If you shared good communication and created a good connection during **Week 2, Winter**, with lots of dates, heart-to-hearts, and sweet lovemaking, then **Week 3, Spring** should go really well. We'll look at this week in two phases: Ovulation and post-Ovulation.

The first day of Spring week is Ovulation. Ovulation *represents* The Moment of Truth. It *represents* connection. The whole female sex cycle supports this *one* day. Her cycle, and therefore your relationship's cycle, is about resting, courting, connecting, creating, and then evaluating, leaving behind what does not serve and keeping what does. While Ovulation lasts only 24 hours, the high she feels should last the week, especially if she is exercising a lot. Endorphins enhance this high in her cycle. Consider working out together in some form, whether it's going to the gym, running on the beach, or playing in the yard.

It is vital that you understand how to support her, and benefit yourself, during this particular phase by continuing to court her. Stay connected and present. At the beginning of the week she is fully presenting herself to you and to the world. This is the climax or orgasm of *her cycle*. Task-wise, she may be sharing a project that she's been working on. Sexually, this is your private party time together that she and her body have been preparing for, the culmination of the attention you've both paid to understanding her rhythm. She is receptive. It's time to respond.

Her senses are heightened at this time. When you pay attention to how your skin feels (no stubble!), how you dress and groom yourself, and how you smell, she will respond with all of her senses. It's time for hot and passionate sex. It is crucial to focus all your sexual energy on her and her alone. This is the time to experiment, to have fun exploring each other's bodies. Be open and willing to try new stuff. Don't worry about not getting it right; just try, and maybe have a few laughs. It's payoff time for all of your attentiveness and support. It's the day to get down and dirty. Be sure birth control is in place.

Here, at Ovulation, she is in her Goddess: magnificent, bold, stunning, and primal. Feed each other's ravenous hunger and don't hold back. Be her majestic animal and her glorious God. Openly give and receive.

The rest of this week is post-Ovulation. Her peak has come and gone, leaving room for her sexual energy to move into a more balanced and comfortable state. If all went well in the two weeks leading up to and including the party, then the rest of the week should be great for you both. Reflecting on all that has happened so far, she'll be feeling satisfied and closer to you than ever. Keep the affection going throughout the day and night for your relationship to stay healthy.

At this phase of her cycle, imagine her as Cleopatra looking out over the land, contemplative and knowing, ready to take action where needed. She is now in her wise leadership mode, so standing side by side with her on this will make her feel supported. Be King to her Queen. Continue to step up as her man and be proud to show off the beautiful woman on your arm. "Yep, she's mine." This is the week to attend a fundraiser or the symphony.

Now is the chance to talk about how your time together was during the height of her sex drive; ask how things are going for her and express how they are going for you. Talk about what your expectations were, sexually and romantically, and ask about hers. Were you both fulfilled? If not, what could you each do differently next month? Post-Ovulation is a great time to work on understanding her desires and exploring and discussing your own. Jot down anything that seems unfinished and revisit it again during next month's **Week 2, Winter**.

This is also the best time to talk about the logistics of your relationship such as finances, plans for the future, family matters, and world views. Do not miss this opportunity, as it is an important foundational piece of your partnership. Be open to learning new communication skills, and your relationship will improve and continue to grow.

As your sweetie moves into **Week 4, Summer**, she'll need some room to breathe as she prepares to observe and let go of some mental and emotional baggage. The best way to support her in this, and get some private time for yourself, is to focus on the tasks around the house that you've been wanting to get to. Every time you take advantage of what can be learned from her cycle, you'll be reminded of all that is in it for you. Remember, working together almost guarantees an overall positive relationship. By continuing to court her, delivering to her mentally, emotionally, and physically, you will discover that committing to another person is the sexiest thing you've ever done in your life.

> The root word of courage is *cor*—the Latin word for heart. In one of its earliest forms, the word courage had a very different definition than it does today. Courage originally meant, "To speak one's mind by telling all one's heart"....Today, courage is more synonymous with being heroic....Heroics is often about putting our life on the line. Ordinary courage is about putting our vulnerability on the line.
>
> —Brené Brown

8. summer

Fire is the origin of stone. By
working the stone with heat,
I am returning it to its source.

—Andy Goldsworthy

week 4
summer
"Fire Season"

KNOWN AS: **PMS** or Pre-Menstrual Syndrome
REPLACED WITH: **"The Fire Walk"**

QUICK VIEW COMPARISONS

- **Week 4 (Days 22–28)**
- **Summer/Fall**
  - **Northern Hemisphere:** July, August, September
  - **Southern Hemisphere:** January, February, March
- **Waning Moon**

KEY WORDS: Irritable, Hot, Protecting and Preserving Self, Purging Thoughts and Emotions

- **Central Theme:** *Emoping*
- **Focus:** To recognize and acknowledge what is presented, what surfaces
- **Symbolism:** Getting rid of what no longer serves or is damaging your essence; balance
- **Intention:** To embrace the purpose and genius of this process

FEMININE CYCLE

- **Hormonal Phase:** Secretory or luteal
- **Hormone Activity:** Estrogen low, progesterone high and

Participate ~ Pinpoint ~ Prevail

then tanks if no pregnancy occurs; testosterone moderate and fluctuating

SUMMER, THE SEASON (COMPARISON)

- **In Nature:** Sun, drought, fire, heat, humidity, thunderstorms, lightning; the Summer Solstice to the Autumnal Equinox begins the slow descent of light toward darkness
- **Foods:** Raw vegetables, fruit, hydrating beverages and light desserts
- **Activity:** Bustling if cool, lethargic if hot

MOON (COMPARISON)

- **Phase to Relate to:** Waning (closing down)
- **Moon and Feminine Cycle Phase:** Last quarter
- **Moon and Feminine Cycle Days:** 22–28 (adjust female cycle days as needed)

CEREMONIAL ENERGIES

- **Four Directions:** South
- **Four Elements:** Fire (passion, heat)
- **Colors:** Bright, neon (hot)
- **Chakras:** Solar Plexus (3), Root (1), and Throat (5)

FEMALE BODY

- **Immune System:** Vulnerable, fragile
- **Overall Energy:** High, with stressed nerves
- **Physically:** Inflamed, loosening and breaking down, nerves electrified, acne surfaces at lymph line along chin
- **Mentally:** Active, sharp, focused, and irritated if disturbed or pressured

Participate ~ Pinpoint ~ Prevail

~ **Emotional Spectrum:** "Pore-ing" or pouring out of pores and tear ducts; on the surface, on edge

~ **Soulfully:** Honoring self and those we care for by acknowledging what is not working

~ **Outward Appearance/Behavior:** Annoyed/impatient

~ **Senses:** All senses heightened

SEX DRIVE

~ **Juices:** Moderate to drying

~ **Nipples:** Becoming sore

~ **Orgasms:** Take longer, less intense, heightened right before the Period

~ **Ideas:** Go for quick-and-to-the-point sex as a stress reliever; stay away from too much verbal communication and stick to sexual stuff you know works well for both of you

OUTLOOK

~ **Overall:** Tends to be negative—the things that don't work in your life are surfacing

~ **Archetypes:** ATHLETE, FIRE WALKER, MONK

~ **Mind Mood Persona:** "Everyone is stupid;" "The world is messed up;" evaluating life

~ **Attitude:** Critical, irritable, sees the glass as half empty, like the Waning Moon

~ **Relationships:** Strained

~ **When Positive:** Reflective and content, like a nice day at the beach

~ **When Challenged:** Judgmental, angry, jealous, and/or irritated, indicating unhappiness, dissatisfaction, or not feeling well

Participate ~ Pinpoint ~ Prevail

SUGGESTIONS FOR YOU

- **Make an intention** to notice when irritation erupts by way of tears, anger, frustration

- **Journal:** Jot down your thoughts and experiences on paper or on your mobile device

- **Be patient with others:** This is your process, not theirs; vent on paper, not onto people

- **Stick with** routines; make no major decisions; get things done

- **Notice and begin to enjoy** the positive aspects of your life—jot them down

CARE REGIMEN SUGGESTIONS

- **Food:** Clean and light for easy digestion and to keep inflammation down

- **Exercise:** Yes!

- **Sleep:** You may feel a little wired, so exercise hard during the day to help you sleep and to take the edge off

- **Beauty:** Skin becoming sensitive for body waxing; acne may be erupting; frowning

- **Clothes:** Wear cool and comfortable (both temperature-wise *and* attractiveness); wear only your classic stand-bys that you love; solids, rather than prints

SUGGESTIONS FOR HIM

- **Stay home** but do your own thing; stick with routine home chores or projects

- **Write down** arising issues to discuss later during **Week 2, Winter**. Listen to and actually *hear* what she has to say

- **No arguing here;** gently and firmly set your boundary if you truly need to

Participate ~ Pinpoint ~ Prevail

- **Absolutely NO name-calling** or badmouthing her behind her back to your friends; when this happens, you have ceased to be her protector
- **Find your *Earth* energy:** Stable and solid supports her important and needed *fire* energy
- **Sexually:** Follow her lead on sex; stick with what works for sure; regular hugs are nice; no pawing or neediness; stay away from sore nipples

Overview
Week 4, Summer

There is a rhyme and a reason for these hot, inflamed days of the fourth week of your cycle, traditionally known as the PMS week. I say "traditionally known" because we've come to think of this week as a syndrome, yet syndrome indicates illness. This week is not an illness, it is a process, and one must have its beginning and ending easily and quickly identified, and the handling of this process honored. I describe this week as Emoping, or an Emotional Period. We purge thoughts and emotions this week, while our internal bodies begin to break down, before purging the physical during **Week 1, Fall** in the form of the Period. Within this Emoping phase of our cycle, we meet three archetypes, the Athlete, the Fire Walker, and the Monk.

Purely and simply, I aim to wipe the idea of PMS off the planet and with it all insulting and derogatory accusations. Every piece of any cycle has a positive purpose and each is a preparation for the next phase. The female monthly recycling system is no different.

Our current practice of blaming relationship problems (and women being angry) on PMS does not fit with the holistic blueprint of the feminine cycle—nor with the cyclical order of nature.

Like a beautiful volcano bringing lava, Mother Nature's fire, to

Participate ~ Pinpoint ~ Prevail

the surface, your core trembles as the body prepares to take down the uterine nest. Impurities from the body, mind, and essence rise to the surface and push their way out, causing skin to break out and nerve ends to feel a bit prickly. Here lies your opportunity to evaluate what you hold dear and what you need to get rid of, discovering your true gifts along the way. As our cycle winds down, a sense of serenity and surrender takes hold, finishing with the desire to be still and serene.

Hormones
Week 4, Summer

You know the saying, "If mama ain't happy, ain't nobody happy!"? This is the week that makes many, many women feel absolutely and insanely out of control and those who live with them feel confused or angry. This confusion or anger can lead into a vicious spiral of heated arguments and attacks. For other women, this week goes completely unnoticed and they wonder what all the fuss is about. Still others are in between. Even if your hormonal changes are subtle, it is important to recognize what is happening with them so that you are conscious about the way you are handling your life throughout the entire month.

Many women choose to ignore these subtle changes, rejecting the idea that hormones might rule our lives. I used to believe the same thing until I figured out that hormones *do* affect me, yet *I* could be the one in control, not my hormones. I discovered that if I *didn't* take charge, then, indeed, the hormones *would* be in charge of me. Control came with understanding my cycle, not denying it.

Your hormones are naturally throwing you into this *Emoping* phase, this *Emotional Period*. It is another part of your natural hormonal landscape that you must travel through. Your experience can vary depending on your preparation and how well you know this section of the road. If you know what is ahead and you are ready, then

Participate ~ Pinpoint ~ Prevail

you'll handle it better and better each time you pass through. Eventually you will come to know it as an outstanding adventure to look forward to! If you haven't prepared and don't know what lies ahead, you may be in for a treacherous journey.

Hormones

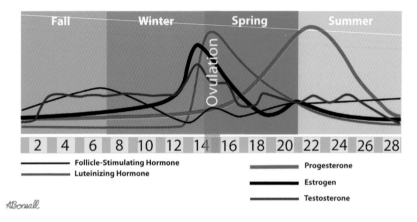

What is causing all this misery? Is it *really* hormones all the time? Is it food? Is it unhappiness? Is it lack of support? Perhaps it is a little of each and more. One thing is for sure: *you* are not crazy. Basically, estrogen and progesterone are the main female hormones that regulate our cycles and sustain a pregnancy, should it happen. Progesterone is the hormone most responsible for maintaining a cushy uterine nest for a baby to incubate in, and estrogen helps with nutrition of the early embryo. When no pregnancy occurs, the dismantling process slowly begins. Estrogen already began its descent back in the third week, but progesterone is still high and energy is maintaining. Testosterone is lower but is also maintaining, so the sex drive follows suit. As the days wear on and no fertilized egg attaches to the uterine wall, progesterone gets the message that it is no longer needed to support the nest and drops drastically. With it go the things we need to purge from our minds and souls in the form of emotions. These emotions and thoughts exit right out of our skin, right out of our tear ducts, and right out of our mouths.

Participate ~ Pinpoint ~ Prevail

This dismantling of the uterus is a powerful action—a forceful wave pushing emotional debris out of our systems before releasing physical debris in the form of blood during **Week 1, Fall**. Remember, estrogen gives you energy and is your natural beautifier. Progesterone is the one keeping everything mellow, balancing the estrogen if it starts to get too high. When in balance, they are natural "feel-good" drugs. So, when our feel-good drugs are taken away, naturally we're a little cranky!

Your issues are real; basically your hormones are pushing them to the surface, encouraging you to deal with them. The question is, are they overly magnified and amplified right now? Have you allowed them to go unaddressed and now they've become a big deal? Perhaps you *have* addressed them many times and you're not being heard. Have you compromised them away in order to not make waves and now you're just mad at yourself for doing so? This is the week to identify what is really happening. The time has come to begin balancing out your cycle experience by honoring who you really are, rather than being what others expect you to be. Addressing issues with honesty as they arise during the other weeks, and establishing your boundaries, will make an enormous difference in how this week goes. You are a Queen. Take charge of your life.

A Word on Estrogen Dominance

High amounts of estrogen are toxic to the body and can create a number of harmful side effects. In addition to many of the symptoms associated with PMS, estrogen dominance has been linked to auto-immune disorders, breast cancer, uterine cancer, infertility, ovarian cysts, and increased blood clotting, and is also associated with acceleration of the aging process, according to Dr. Christiane Northrup.[31] If progesterone is low for some reason, then it can cause estrogen to dominate. When this happens, a potentially dangerous imbalance occurs.

Your doctor will most likely suggest supplementing with bio-identical progesterone, as this hormone has very few side effects, even in high doses.[32]

Participate ~ Pinpoint ~ Prevail

Estrogen dominance has become a somewhat generic catch-all term for many female hormone symptoms, but it is a place to start if you're feeling a little harsh on a regular basis, or more negatively dramatic than feels right. Again, **talk to your health provider** about it if you suspect anything.

Your Rhythm and The Pill

You may have lost a little of your heightened libido normally experienced in **Week 2, Winter** due to the Ovulation-suppressing action of The Pill, but the silver lining in this story is that your fourth week will most likely have fewer aggravating physical and emotional symptoms to experience than if you were *not* on The Pill. The hormonal designs of the various types of birth control pills smooth out the extreme up-and-down pattern of the natural rhythm, thereby smoothing out one's cycle experience. This is particularly good news for those who truly suffer every month during this week.

Fertility Awareness: If You Are NOT on The Pill

You should not be fertile at this time since Ovulation has come and gone, but check with your doctor to be sure. Keep in mind, though, that whether you're on The Pill or not, the only thing that can help prevent the spread of sexually transmitted diseases (STDs) is a condom, and only certain ones at that. Check the label on the box.

Reproduction Comparison: Labor

I liken the process of **Week 4, Summer** to being in labor. Labor is the preparation process of moving a baby into position to be birthed. The baby is pushing its way out during labor, and with it comes strong emotions, irritated nerves, and the "beyond belief" contractions that make your belly feel on fire!

Labor is the ultimate expression of **Week 4, Summer**. This Emoping portion of our rhythmic cycle is simply a much smaller reflection of labor. The Period during **Week 1, Fall** is the smaller substitute for

Participate ~ Pinpoint ~ Prevail

birthing. When a baby is not being birthed, the uterine nest *is*, in the form of blood.

We don't call labor a "syndrome," so why on Earth do we call the Pre-Period week a syndrome? Syndrome implies *disorder*. This is exactly the opposite from what it is: *perfect order.* We can't deliver a baby naturally without labor, and we don't bleed without the emotional labor or *Emoping*—purging our emotions first.

Characteristics
Week 4, Summer

Reminder: The 4s4w strategy, or system, was created for the sole purpose of putting the female cycle into perspective in order to relate our experiences to its week-to-week and day-to-day changes and remembering how they go without too much effort.

Each woman is different and ultimately must identify and adjust her own rhythm, but the hormonal influences of each phase tend to have the general characteristics of the seasons. The 4s4w system attempts to add meaning to these characteristics.

The Feminine Cycle (Days 22–28)

I describe the traits for **Week 4, Summer** as negative; however, it is not this week of the feminine cycle that is the problem. *It is doing exactly what it is supposed to be doing: dumping *emotional* trash now, in preparation for dumping *physical* trash later—the stuff that is no longer needed in your body. This is a healthy recycling process. *Your* general viewpoint and *that of the masses* is the adjustment that needs to happen here, not your cycle. We've not been taught to understand what is so amazing about this portion of the cycle so we have had no idea how to embrace it. Transforming the way you *think* about it, and *preparing* for it during the prior weeks, will help immensely to im-

Participate ~ Pinpoint ~ Prevail

prove your experience of this week.

When I compare **Week 4, Summer** to the heat of the Summer season, I don't mean that you are *literally* hot in temperature, although I do notice that my temperature gauge can feel amplified because my nerves are on the surface, so to speak. So if I'm cold, for instance, I am more cold than usual. If I'm hot, I am more hot than usual. I use "the hottest day of the year" as an *analogy* for **Week 4, Summer** to explain what this week can feel like to us women. The irritation and impatience is similar to what one would experience when outside on the hottest day of the year. We become negatively sensitive to noise, light, touch, smell, people, and other energy in general. On the hottest day of the year we don't like too much touching, too much attention, too many demands—we're just too hot and sticky!

> This is the time of my cycle when I think everyone is just stupid!
>
> —Moriah Davis

During this **Week 4, Summer** of our cycle, we resist energy *coming in* because so much inside is pushing itself *out*. We're edgy because our nerves feel pushed to the edge. Emotions are trying to push their way right out through our pores.

By the end of this week you'll most likely be feeling very internal, beginning to evaluate all the thoughts and feelings that have risen to the surface. Creating a quiet space to go inward is ideal. This is a great time to reclaim or affirm your healthy boundaries.

Participate ~ Pinpoint ~ Prevail

How the *Characteristics* of Summer, the Moon and the Feminine Cycle Relate

Days and Nights: Just as the Winter Solstice is the darkest day of the year but signifies the slow ascent into light (the *days* begin to lengthen), the Summer Solstice is the lightest day of the year and signifies the slow descent into darkness (the *nights* begin to lengthen). As the brilliant Sun sears through the Summer months, the days get hotter as Summer heads toward Autumn. Like a Waning Moon lessening its light, going toward the darkness of the New Moon, you, my dear, must go from feeling light and sporty to subdued and self-contained as you enter the deepest phase of your cycle. Take all that moonlight for yourself and use it as an internal beacon to light the way for new discoveries about YOU. Explore. Let the heat of mid- to late-Summer be your guide.

Hot and Sticky: *Warm* Summer days inspire us to be outside with family and friends, camping, playing volleyball, or riding bikes. *Warm* Summer nights can hold some of the most magical memories of our lives. *Hot* days and nights can drain and irritate.

I love the idea of Summer and all the fun of Summer, but when it is very hot, it is my least favorite time of the year. It's hot. It's sticky. I'm irritable and my head hurts. Getting errands done in this heat *gets* to me in short order. When it is this hot, the heat is all anyone in town talks about. It's hard for us to think about anything else because it is so darn hot!

It is 107°F as I write this here in Southern Oregon where I live, which is a perfect example of the fourth week of the female cycle. These are called the Dog Days of Summer and the term "bitch" gets thrown around a little too easily during this time in our cycles. Throughout the actual Summer season we can retreat to our air-conditioned homes, but there is no escaping these hot spots in our natural rhythm. We need to learn how to manage the heat of our feminine cycle instead of ignoring it or masking it with medication. While I think ibuprofen is great stuff to assist you in getting through discomfort if really needed, it is not going to solve your problems and

Participate ~ Pinpoint ~ Prevail

has its own set of long-term health concerns.[33] It's time to face the heat of your cycle by finding higher ground.

Outdoor Activities: The beginning of Summer generally starts out energetically. Families are excited that school is out and in many places the weather is outstanding and hasn't yet gotten crazy-hot. We launch straight into some sort of vacation or bee-line it to the beach. In the same way, the beginning of this phase of your cycle is an active time, as your hormones still have you feeling up and your energy is high. Like the Summer Sun, your cycle will get more intense before you complete the circle.

Thunder, Lightning, and Fireworks: The electricity that crackles and sparks the air during Summer storms matches the electrical feel of nerves pressing against skin as emotions run rampant. Heated, emotional arguments aren't called "fireworks" for nothing.

The atmospheric pressure we feel from heavy cloud cover before a storm is not much different from the pressure of water weight gain and the swelling of sinuses we often experience when on the brink of our Periods.

Preparing for Fall: The end of Summer brings on the need to prepare—for the harvest, back to school, vacation's end, and more. Shopping for school and work clothes, gathering supplies, getting schedules straight, organizing car pools, and dealing with extra paperwork creates a flurry of "getting ready" activity. The feminine cycle **Week 4, Summer** provides us with the opportunity to prepare for our Periods by tying up loose ends before shutting down our cycles. I get sharply focused on finishing projects, paying bills, organizing work and home projects, and clearing the decks, in the same way that I do before going on a vacation. A deadline is coming—and you want to be ready for it.

Garage Sales and Organizing: Summer is the season for garage sales. We continue our third-week *Spring cleaning* by taking action on our decisions. We'll keep some things and let go of others. Perhaps you'll finally get rid of the old couch, canoe, or painting that you held on to for way too long.

Participate ~ Pinpoint ~ Prevail

This is the time to get serious about getting rid of stuff because you are going into Fall and Winter. If you don't get rid of things now, you'll most likely not get rid of them until next year, if at all. The relief of having an organized space, easy access to what you *do* have stored, and being able to park in the garage, is immeasurable.

In this same way, during this part of your cycle, you are evaluating and eliminating; you are deciding what emotions serve you and what needs to go. A great deal of this evaluation is considering our purpose and the gifts we have to offer to the world. Are we fulfilling our life goals? Are we at the right job? Are we with the right partner? Are we living in the right town? This is our "GPS" talking, luring us back to our spiritual center, to our personal place of power, true happiness, and well-being.

Final Thoughts on Comparisons

It's fairly common for a pregnant woman to clean like crazy before giving birth. Something instinctive kicks in with a "now or never" urgency. Nature wants a newborn to have a proper nest and for a mother to feel settled and prepared when she gives birth. I notice that this same phenomenon happens with me every month. I have enormous energy to do these types of chores (sorting, organizing, and deciding) throughout this week. I see my cleaning frenzy or project-finishing as a sign that my Period is coming soon. Perhaps our body aches are a signal to hurry up, because our down time is impending. The cycle is nearly complete.

> **Feelings of irritation and discomfort** experienced in **Week 4, Summer** of the feminine cycle are similar to the feelings in the Summer season, as if no shade exists. This tends to be the best phase for staying cool by sweating out (or crying out) what no longer serves you and your life path.

Participate ~ Pinpoint ~ Prevail

Symbolic Transitions & Influences
Week 4, Summer

Since **Week 4, Summer** is part of a cycle in motion, the first day of the week is different from the last day of the week. Our physical bodies *and* our Mind Moods change daily.

Influences on the Body: Chaotic; Turbulent

- Energy
- Internal Combustion: Triggering Emotion
- Spotting

You may find yourself *running* into **Week 4, Summer**, feeling energetic from standing your tallest and finding your voice during **Week 3, Spring**. This **Spring**-to-**Summer** outdoor season comparison suggests it is a great time to be active.

You should be feeling good at the beginning of this week, so it is vital to get cardio exercise in now. Try kicking your workouts up a notch in order to help you direct some of the intensity that will soon come out in a day or two, when your progesterone tanks. This high energy creates a great opportunity for getting things done. It also encourages your circulation to keep things moving *through* you so that they can move *out* of you easily when the time comes.

Eating clean foods to prevent inflammation, in addition to working out and playing sports, is one way to feel great and prepare for the hotter days ahead. You'll need down time when your Period starts in a week. Once you enter your more challenging days, you may find that continuing to exercise is a great way to burn off feelings of anger or frustration as they surface.

Since you are sharply focused on each task or activity you take on,

Participate ~ Pinpoint ~ Prevail

you'll feel quite accomplished when you take advantage of the guidance this Emoping week offers you to recycle physically, emotionally, mentally, and soulfully.

Internal Combustion

It may be hard to distinguish what is causing stress this week because the physical, the emotional, and the mental processes work together to dislodge what is no longer needed in all areas. One thing is for sure: the break-down of your uterine nest must happen, which in turn can trigger a domino effect of mental and emotional surprises. Since the physical body sometimes seems to act before we have a chance to stop it, in order to evaluate what is happening, let's first explore the *physical* manifestations and discomforts that can happen when our hormones start to tank.

This Emoping phase of your feminine cycle equates to the Waning Moon phase and enters your life energetically, yet silently, from a hormonal high point once your body figures out you are not pregnant. Catching you unaware, your body experience changes as your uterine lining begins to dismantle. This will last until you start your Period in **Week 1, Fall**, when the entire nest gets flushed out in the form of blood.

Think of this **Week 4, Summer** as similar to gathering your trash and recycling from your home and taking it out to curbside, where it sits until it is picked up. Think of next week, **Week 1, Fall**, as the action of the garbage and recycling trucks actually coming around and

Participate ~ Pinpoint ~ Prevail

taking away the trash and recycling that you set out at curbside. Another analogy is labor and delivery. The baby can't be birthed until it settles into the birthing canal. This week compares to labor and next week compares to birthing. There is a whole lot of rumbling going on inside of you during this week in preparation for the final purge.

As the nest breaks down, Nature's blueprint calls on our bodies to initiate an investigation into all of the trash we need to dump, items we need to keep, and thoughts we need to recycle into a healthier viewpoint in order to support our highest good and greatest gifts. It does so by bringing it all to the surface in a very sensory way. I go from feeling active to strongly competitive to downright cranky. My nerves are on edge, so I'm edgy! My thoughts are next, trying to make their way out of my mouth, tear ducts, and pores as mixed-up emotions. My skin is tender to the touch, so I don't want my honey's body pushed up too close to me, day or night, in the same way that I don't want to be touched when I'm sweating during the hottest day of the year! Before I know it I'm too bloated, too sticky, and too touchy.

Any of us might sadden easily and purge the emotion by crying. We might experience the emotion by feeling our blood boil and then lashing out in anger with yelling, sarcasm, or (hopefully not) throwing dishes across the room. We're hot, irritable, and sweaty. This purging serves as a tool to keep us healthy, so we must learn how to manage and direct it.

Spotting

As your uterus breaks down and gets closer to completely purging, you may experience small signs of blood, telling you that your Period is coming any time now. If it is dark, dark blood, this is old blood being washed out. Any spotting can feel unsettling, so it's important to know what it means. Ask your health provider questions and be kind to yourself. Slow down into stillness, tune in to the signs of your rhythm and, like a good Girl Scout, be prepared. Make sure to have the right supplies with you at all times.

Participate ~ Pinpoint ~ Prevail

Influences on the Mind and Soul: The Gift of Transformation

Mind Moods and ARCHETYPES

- ATHLETE
- Fire Season: Warrior Fire Goddess
- FIRE WALKER
- THE MONK: Fire Purification Days
- Your Authentic Female

Week 4, Summer is the accumulation of all energies from Weeks 1, 2, and 3. You'll have a lot of catching up to do in dealing with the choices and circumstances of years and years of physical and nutritional imbalance, lack of body information, or hormonal imbalance due to birth control pills, pregnancy, and nursing. Added to that is the mental and emotional load of fear, sadness, distrust, disappointment, wounded womb, loss of boundaries, criticism when you got and get angry, criticism for being a woman, and secret expectations (of epic proportions) that you've simply stored, gotten used to, and think of as normal. It might be culturally normal, but it's not natural. Our female cycle blueprint is guiding us to Heaven on Earth, not Hell on wheels.

ATHLETE

From the ultimate beauty and brains Goddess to the Wise Woman and World Leader of **Week 3, Spring,** it is no wonder that a competitive streak kicks

Participate ~ Pinpoint ~ Prevail

in to keep you going at the starting gate of **Week 4, Summer**. Since you'll be losing your feel-good drugs, estrogen and progesterone, your drive and vitality may hang on and continue as a bit aggressive and high-strung. Take advantage of these tools to work out like crazy, play sports, get that project done, or perhaps even go for that raise.

As your powerful fire energy ignites, you'll need to be careful not to carry your Olympic torch into the arena of confrontation and combativeness. The only person you need to be competing with is yourself. Challenge your ability to self-observe so that you can take responsibility for your actions and make good decisions.

Fire Season: Warrior Fire Goddess

This hot and electric week is our Fire Season, and the Warrior Fire Goddess in you could show up like an out-of-control wildfire. If left unchecked, she'll be spreading her flames whichever way the wind is blowing. The goal is to use your fire to cleanse and purify, to allow it to burn away the cluttered underbrush of a forest without killing the mature trees and destroying everything in its path. When we fail to control the burn, it is easy to find ourselves stuck in our own inferno, allowing it to consume us, to extinguish our inner beauty. It is important that we not let it take us to an ugly place that no longer resembles who we are.

A keen sense of awareness is developing if you will let it. This is the week when you are evaluating your relationships and situations.

Has your partner continued to court you every month? Are you being heard when you communicate? Are you spending time on a dead-end relationship or job, or on one without the outcome you're seeking? Are you safer in a relationship or alone? Do you like yourself when you are with your partner? Have you set and communicated boundaries that clarify your relationships? Regarding life choices, are you currently at your best? Are you true to yourself or are you needing to compromise or abandon your core values?

Participate ~ Pinpoint ~ Prevail

FIRE WALKER

As your progesterone drops and your uterine nest begins to disassemble, deeper thoughts or emotions, which otherwise go through a mind-filtering process (in order to flow out of you a little more diplomatically or gracefully), burst out unrefined and raw. The trick is to figure out whether the unfiltered words or force behind your thoughts are really truth for you, or if they are truth coated in protection, or simply the irritation of not feeling well.

The Fire Walk begins this evaluation process. It is the time when I first realize I have come upon the "hottest" days of my cycle. The Fire Walk begins the moment I find myself crying over something I would not otherwise cry over. Sometimes I have an almost uncontrollable urge to sob. Maybe I've just snapped at someone, feeling a bit of anger pulse through my veins. When something like this happens to you, you must learn to stop and identify it as the starting point of your Fire Walk. For the next couple of days your main job is to watch for hot spots like these.

Once I identify the beginning of my Fire Walk, I know that it is best to allow myself to cry in a controlled setting, off by myself. The purging feels like a necessary step toward discovering what is deep within me that needs attention, or it is simply a way to relieve stress. We only have about seven days to get through this Emoping phase of our cycle, our fourth week, so when my Fire Walk hits, I want to get

Participate ~ Pinpoint ~ Prevail

moving with the processing of it. Wishing it would go away, or being confused by it, only compounds the distress over time.

Outbursts mean something. Lashing out is often a fight against our own uncomfortable bodies or an underlying issue or value that is coming to the surface. You are at your strongest, yet most vulnerable, during these fiery days and are guarding and holding on to your Authentic Self as your body tissue breaks down. You may discover that you've given too much away and feel challenged by your past generosity of self. You may want to get rid of the anger behind your issues, but also feel justified (and rightly so) in keeping true to your desires. Once here, I need to tread carefully through this zone, stepping back, taking a breath if needed, long enough to slow down and evaluate.

Because this is Fire Season, I need to be careful about starting fires to begin with, contain them where needed, and put them out if they are threatening to burn out of control. This is the time when life's demands push us to declare, "Enough is enough!" This is an excellent time to sort out your feelings in writing or text.

Heat and Heart represent passion, do they not? Passion can explode as rage, love, devotion, creativity, or protection. As an accomplished 4s4w Fire Walker, I now know how to direct and manage my passion, rather than letting it direct and manage me. I've learned to identify the day my Fire Walk begins, be observant, gather the gifts that surface, and then decide how to address them during the Fire Purification Days that follow. If I don't identify this day I can prolong the process, miss dealing with my issues, and stuff them away for yet another month. I then lose out on the chance to get in alignment with my heart's true desires.

If I've slept on a hot spot issue, yet wake up in the morning and still find a challenge pressing, then I might go ahead and address it because perhaps I'm not brave enough to confront the situation during other times of my cycle. Sometimes our fire is needed as fuel to help us speak up. Other times I'll wake up and know (from past experience) that the best thing to do is to write it all down in my journal to discuss during my better communication time, **Week 2, Winter**. My rule of thumb is that if I'm angry, it might be the time I

> Lots of people want to ride with you in the limo, but what you want is someone who will take the bus with you when the limo breaks down.
>
> —Oprah Winfrey

Participate ~ Pinpoint ~ Prevail

want to speak, but it is the absolute worst time *to* speak and I will almost always regret it later. Make this mistake too many times and the consequences will eventually teach you to stop, or you will burn your bridges.

Many people blast others away with their silence, arrogance, or cold looks, thinking they are taking the superior road. Shutting someone out, acting fed up, ignoring someone altogether, controlling how much time passes before responding to a call or email, being a martyr (doing it yourself because everyone else is too lame), or gossiping behind someone's back are all cruel forms of getting back at someone or acting out. Your silence or sideways behaviors often speak louder than words.

Which type are you? How do you release? Write down what you're angry or disappointed about so that you can identify these things in a couple of weeks when your communication skills are not competing with Emoping. Of course, also write down what you're pleased about! It is even more important to communicate this message—the good stuff is too often overlooked.

The Fire Walk is not only about stepping gingerly through your external life, but it takes you on a journey into the core of *you*. As you navigate the hot bed of coals, you'll discover pieces that you want to preserve and protect. Like a Mama Bear guarding her cub, you are becoming protective of yourself and your future offspring, shielding your power core, keeping what is solely yours, and hanging on to what you need so that it does not get washed out with the strong current of debris. You are in survival mode and want others to hear your truth and honor your principles and boundaries. When we become adept Fire Walkers, we learn to trust our own wisdom with every step. This is the beauty of **Week 4, Summer.**

These hot spots are also indicators of your gifts that you've not yet recognized, by way of your weaknesses, deeply-rooted, unresolved challenges, built-up resentments, or simply mundane things that need attending to.

Ken Page, LCSW, teaches us that our core gifts can usually be

Participate ~ Pinpoint ~ Prevail

found in the places of our deepest sensitivity, longing and passion—our most painful wounds and insecurities. By taking an opposite approach to our challenges, reframing a weakness as a strength, we can begin to attract the kinds of relationships we desire.[34]

For instance, betrayal is something that can be very difficult to reconcile or get over. If you find anger surfacing during your fourth week due to being lied to (and you thought you were over it), you may wonder why it happened, be mad at yourself for allowing it to happen, feel humiliated, or be frustrated that you continue to obsess over it. By reframing this scenario to be about a strength, rather than a weakness, you may discover that the reason you are upset is because you are a loyal and honest person and don't do this type of behavior to others. Your strengths and gifts are loyalty and honesty. This is a good thing for which you will definitely want to honor yourself!

When you begin to glean your strengths from what feel like negative emotions or wounds, you will begin to understand where your authenticity lies, what an awesome person you are, and therefore will know your true core gifts.

The Monk: Fire Purification Days

Once I've made it through the bed of hot lava, carrying out my discoveries to take into my Fire Purification Days, I've learned it is best to shut it all down and close the curtains. It feels right to get centered and quiet now. I imagine myself as a Monk who turns my active *or* down times into a meditation practice.

I love the energy and mental sharpness this week provides and I have discovered that I prefer to work alone to get projects done. I am more productive this way. As my body's focus goes inward, it makes sense to go inward with my thoughts and razor-sharp focus. If I need to communicate with others, it seems to take too much effort and I have a hard time articulating what I need.

Like the Moon gathering the last morsels of light for herself as she goes into her New Moon state, going inward whenever possible is the best way for me to take a look at my issues. The quiet helps

Participate ~ Pinpoint ~ Prevail

me to deal with my frustrations that continue to surface out of the blue. It is easier for me to notice them and block out stimulation that irritates me if I get into a habit of being internal, a habit of looking at my *self*. It makes it simpler to write down my experiences. It makes it easier for me to *not react* to someone else's behavior, which may or may not be appropriate.

I actually get into *not* speaking at all when I don't need to. Others don't know I'm doing this, as I don't need to be extreme about it and inconvenience *them*; but I don't make extra phone calls, sing to the radio, or go to the bank or coffee with friends, etc., unless it is absolutely necessary. I'm identifying *my* stuff while preparing for and honoring the bleeding days to come, where I allow myself to *let it all go*.

By getting quiet, I'm able to sort out fact from fiction in my mind in order to identify what no longer serves me, what I want out of life, and how I need to proceed.

Taking my Fire Walk observations into my solitude, I turn to my womb for help, the warm incubator of transformation. With my mind's eye I place my findings inside. As my uterine nest breaks down in preparation for release, the fire in my belly begins to cleanse my challenges of their muck in a symbolic bonfire, purifying what is meant to remain, the real jewels of this experience. It is at this juncture when my greatest gifts to offer to the world are revealed to me.

Your Authentic Female: Transitioning to Week 1, Fall

I remember an analogy that the spiritual leader Gangaji once relayed.

Participate ~ Pinpoint ~ Prevail

She said that there are two ways to approach an ocean wave. You can go straight out into the water and let yourself get hit by a wave, or you can dive down into the water at the base of the wave before it hits. If you allow the wave to hit you, you'll get knocked over and thrashed around inside of the whitewash until the turbulence is over. You may even feel like you're going to drown. But if you dive down instead, and keep going until you are touching the sand below, allowing the chaos of the wave to wash right over you, there you'll find calm; there you'll find peace.

In the stillness is where the truth rises. In this, we find not what is "normal" but what is natural.

—Sandi Weber

Sitting in stillness, you are allowing the truth of who you are to materialize. Here you will find calm and peace. By sinking into your core self, allowing the chaos of your hormones, your body aches, your mental stresses, as well as your insecurities, your history, and societal expectations to wash right over you, a treasure at the bottom of your ocean will be discovered—a message in a bottle—your Authentic Female. Bring her to the surface. Over time, by following your feminine cycle blueprint, you'll slowly bring all facets of her to the surface in order to serve your life's purpose. The more of her you allow yourself to become, the less debris you'll need to purge as time unfolds.

As you finish **Week 4, Summer** and head into your resting phase of **Week 1, Fall**, I encourage your Authentic Female to unearth your Sacred Feminine qualities, to hold all of the women who have come before you in reverence, and to bond with your sisters in alliance and appreciation. Together we can share Moon Lodge time once again.

Adjusting the Days of This Week

Once you start your Period, you'll be able to calculate how many cycle days were in your rhythm. Once you have tracked for a few months, you'll know your average. If you are able to figure out when you Ovulate, then count from there until you start your Period. If it is fourteen days, then your Spring Week was probably seven days, as was your Summer Week. Once you're able to identify the characteristics of your rhythmic blueprint, you'll get better and better at knowing how many days are in your seasonal weeks.

Participate ~ Pinpoint ~ Prevail

To-Do List
Week 4, Summer

Activities

- ◠ Upon awakening, take just a couple of minutes to
  - Figure out what cycle day you are on
  - Acknowledge what is basically happening with your hormones
  - Set an intention for the day regarding your health and well-being

- ◠ Understand the gifts and purpose of this week (and every week).

- ◠ Be on the lookout during this week for the first day of your Fire Walk.

- ◠ Focus on being attentive to your reactions and responses. Begin to notice exactly what triggers you and when it happens. Is it early in the week or closer to your Period?

- ◠ Allow your thoughts to surface.

- ◠ Notice which of your boundaries have gone missing or have been crossed. Identify them.

- ◠ Keep a notepad with you at all times to jot down thoughts and refer to them later.

- ◠ Make journaling a habit. This will be your busiest writing time. Voicing on paper is one of the best tools to use for identifying what you need to communicate. The better you get at this, the faster you'll smooth out your cycle extremes while getting centered in your feminine power core.

Participate ~ Pinpoint ~ Prevail

∽ Vent on paper, not on people.

∽ Make an intention to be patient with others—this is your process, not theirs.

∽ Stick with routines; this is a great time to clean the house or pay bills; tie up loose ends.

∽ Notice and begin to enjoy the positive aspects of your life—jot them down.

∽ Drink teas that are calming, relaxing, and good for your womb health.

∽ Hard exercise during the day will help you sleep deeply, as you may feel a little wired.

∽ Skin may become sensitive for body waxing or tattoos; acne may be surfacing, especially around the jawline where lymph nodes are purging impurities.

∽ Get busy cleaning out cupboards, drawers, or closets to get rid of things you don't need, organizing your life and reducing clutter; reducing clutter reduces chaos and the feeling of life being out of control; by taking charge of your cupboards, you are symbolically taking charge of your life.

∽ Follow the assignments of the other weeks: lying low, going on date nights, and standing in your power. You'll be better prepared for **Week 4, Summer**.

∽ Notice how you communicate during other weeks of your cycle as well. This will begin to give you a good overall view of your communication pattern. Are you communicating when you need to (and honestly), or are you swinging from one extreme to another, negotiating excessively one week and then over-controlling during another? Are you able to express emotions and thoughts well in order to keep from exploding during this fourth week? Understand that it is *your* responsibility to identify what your short-comings are in communication

Participate ~ Pinpoint ~ Prevail

and to begin improving them. It's crucial, when in relationship to others, to own what is yours and to know what is not.

∾ Prepare for every seasonal week of your cycle.

∾ Thank your beautiful body for its ability to recycle. It's what keeps you healthy.

Food

Avoiding foods that cause inflammation, such as sugar, is probably going to be one of the major things to start paying attention to. The more inflamed your body is, the harder it will be for pent-up emotions to escape with comfort. Remember that Spring cleaning? Do it during the second half of **Week 3, Spring** and your **Week 4, Summer** will be much smoother.

Think Summer dishes. Light, clean foods are a must during this week, as well as in the few days leading up to it. Salads and vegetarian dishes should dominate. Please read the 4s4w supplemental book, *Food for a Female Planet*.

Digestion

I find that, a few days before my Period starts, my digestion begins to become sensitive to raw onions, garlic, and spicy foods. Everything is shutting down; go easy on your system. Eat easy-to-digest stuff. Bowels also begin to loosen up and break things down.

Sleep

You may feel wired, but get as much sleep as you can to help you through the Fire Purification Days.

Exercise

Exercising hard during this week feels good in order to defray some of the intensity of your emotions. Since you'll be lying low in the

Participate ~ Pinpoint ~ Prevail

upcoming week, you will begin to see this as necessary "exercise reserves."

Relationships

This is the week that relationships get strained the most. Both people need to understand what is going on and follow their suggested regimens. Sex without a lot of communication can take some of the edge off between the two of you. This is not a good week to share thoughts on your sex life or relationship in general, although it is a good week to take note of your relationship likes and dislikes.

Sex

You may find you have a burst of heightened libido just before your Period begins because your testosterone surges slightly here. Go for it! Sex during this time is a great stress reliever. I find it is best to just get physical, without a lot of conversation or super romance. If you feel romantic, though, by all means express your desire for your mate! This type of warmth will most likely be quite welcomed at this juncture of your sex cycle. Stick with what works to avoid arguments or frustration.

Letting Go of PMS

In order to embrace your Fire Purification Days, you are going to need to let go of the concept of PMS, unless you truly suffer. It is time for all of us to change our *minds* about this. Healer and author Janis Hunt Johnson teaches something very interesting in her book *Five Smooth Stones*—to not allow illness to attach itself to your being. The 4s4w blueprint invites you to get to the source of many of your challenges before they turn into problems by tracking your cycle and addressing your life as it presents itself. Like surfing, you must get good at riding the waves or they will clobber you in unexpected and sometimes dangerous ways. Try tracking before you decide to allow PMS to be an integral part of who you are. Take your tracker findings to your health practitioner so that she can better assist you with your feminine body needs.

Attitude

For this **Summer** chapter heading I chose the quote, "Fire is the origin of stone" by eco-artist Andy Goldsworthy because it so beautifully shows my point—that our authentic selves may just need the volcanic rumblings and discomfort of heat in order to unearth our true passions, gifts, and values. Shaking up body chemistry and confidence, eroding layers of habits and rationalizations until we reach the source of who we are, we can begin to draw and carry the lava of raw vulnerability from our core beings to the surface, erupting after lying dormant for too long.

Here we are given the opportunity to stand in and face the fire of truth, follow the flames and stand in the glow of the embers. The heat or irritation you're feeling is showing you the way to your life satisfaction and personal enlightenment. It's your flashlight, the light bulb that goes off in your head when you realize that your emotional pain is showing you your boundaries and self-worth. Pay attention to this light bulb!

By shining a light on what is really bothering you, or what is actually ailing you, this trigger can *enlighten* you to get rid of it, handle it differently, shift the energy around it, heal it, speak out about it later, or, minimally, just observe it with the knowledge that "this too shall pass." The goal is not to wish it all away, but to facilitate movement in passing through, or positioning it in its proper place. Once you've gotten rid of what is no longer needed, your gifts will begin to surface. In this way, your focus during this **Week 4, Summer** will go

Participate ~ Pinpoint ~ Prevail

from everything being *wrong* with you and your life to honoring everything that is *right* with you and your life.

Like the mythological Phoenix bird, each month you can rise up transformed, out of the ashes, and start anew. This is your feminine *recycling* system in beautiful form and motion.

Get the Help You Need

Since **Week 4, Summer** is an emotionally cleansing time, it is important to honor and facilitate this to happen in a healthy way. Sometimes it is just *built-up stress* that needs to be released, or it will get stored in your body and eventually become dis-ease. Sometimes you've got *issues* that you need to deal with. If you find yourself having a hard time telling the difference, it's time to seek some professional help. Professional help does *not* mean you're crazy! It is no different from getting an electrician to come in to fix the connection after you've already tried changing the light bulb. It's no different from talking to your doctor about your health after you've tracked your cycle (or even before). Your mind and soul need attention and you need to have a "go-to" person.

Most of the time our go-to person is a girlfriend, sister, or mother. This is fine at first and, in my opinion, the healthiest place to start—*if* they are healthy themselves. They will give you the best advice they can give. On the other hand, a counselor or therapist will give you *tools* to help you turn things around. Their only job is to serve and assist you to get on a healthy track. Or perhaps your hormones truly *are* imbalanced. Your general physician may be able to identify why and do something about it, or refer you to the right specialist.

Participate ~ Pinpoint ~ Prevail

Remember the concept of Combination Health? One solution is not going to be the only solution. We have to keep experimenting and tweaking what works for us. Perhaps just doing an art project or getting a massage will help you to release stress and also work out a problem. Maybe a ceremony of some kind will help you with the symbolism of what is happening. I suggest going to your place of worship, whether it is organized indoors or hiking outdoors, to open what has been shut for too long, which may *then* allow you to figure out why it was shut to begin with.

YOU have to be your best healthcare provider and advocate. A doctor or therapist or sister or massage or art project can help you all day long—but if you're staying up all night, getting very little sleep and living on sugar and caffeine, then there isn't a thing in the world that anyone can do to help you. You're going to throw your hormones out of whack, look like crap, and mess up your relationships. It's time to discover what should be naturally occurring for you rather than experiencing hardships you may be creating unnecessarily through unhealthy choices prior to this week. YOU are the only person who can truly tap into and identify what is going on for you here. It's time to grab hold of your journal and make use of it.

Preparing for Next Week

As you approach the end of your cycle, then begin again with **Week 1, Fall**, it is time to combine your health strategies for maintaining this week and preparing for the next.

Both **Summer** and **Fall** weeks require keeping your inflammation down, which means keeping your food choices clean. In both cases you're purging, so you don't want to be adding junk to your system. When you're deep cleaning your house, the last thing you want is for someone to walk in wearing muddy boots.

You are going to rest next week, so be sure to get everything done this week that will help you to do that. No procrastinating.

Participate ~ Pinpoint ~ Prevail

Personal Inquiry
Week 4, Summer

How do you feel physically this week?

How often did your *Mind Moods* change throughout the week?

Did you notice when your Fire Walk happened?

Were you able to observe your Fire Prevention Days?

What issues surfaced for you?

What did you let go of?

What remains to be discussed in **Week 2, Winter**?

Who and what behaviors do you resent? Make a list.

How did you participate in creating this resentment?

 Did you over-compromise?

Where did you give your power away?

How often did you put your attention on others' needs, only to abandon your own?

When did you not follow your intuition or instincts?

Are there places where you should take responsibility rather than blame and shame?

Are you able to have compassion for yourself, knowing that you're doing the best that you can?

Participate ~ Pinpoint ~ Prevail

The Fire Walk

I'm getting clear on what to keep
Purging out what I don't need
'Cause something's turning up the
heat
I'm getting ready for my bleed!

With the waning of the Moon
I protect the essence that is me
Release emotions and take note
Embrace where I'm supposed to be

Barefoot with a raw intent
Letting loose and dancing free
Naked as the Summer time
The Fire Walk will balance me.

—Sylvia Seroussi Chatroux, M.D.
Poetica Press

Participate ~ Pinpoint ~ Prevail

The ManGuide

Week 4, Summer

"Teammate"

This is your lady's Fire Walk week, when her deepest concerns rise to the surface to be noticed and evaluated. Since this is the week that *traditionally* tends to cause turmoil between couples, I'm going to spend more time on this ManGuide than I do in the other weeks. I feel confident that, over time, you will begin to see the perfection of this amazing phase and the rich opportunity it also brings you to evaluate your deepest concerns in order to co-create the relationship you've always desired.

Every cycle goes through a problem-solving, or descending, stage before it rests and builds, and the feminine cycle is no different. Every relationship is also cyclical in nature and, in order for them to survive when life becomes very real, we must get as good at problem-solving as we are at building a relationship when things are exciting. This deconstructing phase of her cycle offers the perfect opening for you to grasp where you bump heads with each other and where you work well together when on auto-pilot. Her laser-focused heat is her own process, so rather than try to escape it, absorb it, or criticize it, simply observe it. You may end up with some insight and clarity on what to discuss during the heart-to-hearts of **Week 2, Winter**, and your mind-to-minds in **Week 3, Spring**. Keep in mind that you probably have your times of struggle and anger, as well. When you are patient with each other, it is easier to not take things personally while you work problems through to a positive solution.

The best thing you can do this week is to stay consistent and steady, focusing on tasks around the house that need no direction or instruction from her. Find your EARTH energy; stable and solid is the way to support her FIRE energy this week. Accomplishing things that have needed tending to will most likely please her greatly and relieve her stress, as well as support your inner masculinity. Feeling good about what *you* are doing, and understanding her 4s4w recycling progression, will enable you to show up as a man who actually *enjoys* his mate's process. If and when an issue comes your way, you'll more easily identify it as a hot spot that needs further discussion during **Week 2, Winter**. Write it down. Her concerns are real and are gifts to both of you, even if they aren't pretty or packaged in her kindest way. The ability to face conflict and to initiate problem-solving is one of the most attractive behaviors you can develop, because it shows her that you have a desire to be in and protect your relationship with her. In her mind, when you fight to keep your love union and family together in a healthy manner, you are showing the highest form of bravery. When you fight to keep her by doing the active work to keep your relationship good, stick up for her behind her back, support her endeavors, protect her rights as a woman, and reserve your sexual focus for her alone, you are demonstrating a colossal, hunky-kind-of-warrior sexy.

It's important to understand that, for her, this week is about survival mode. When we get down to the raw nature of it, she is subconsciously protecting herself by protecting her values if she detects that they are being compromised. If she feels they are unraveling, she begins to feel unsafe and a bit out of control of her survival and that of her children or other family. While others may innocently ask her to make them a sandwich, she is hanging on, tooth and nail, deciding whether that request is just one too many to leave her with any sort of identity. She's in a bit of a crisis at this juncture. She wants to eliminate unneeded junk and self-sabotaging behaviors from her system, but she doesn't want to lose the things she holds precious to her well-being in the long run. She has an internal GPS that focuses on the happiness of every member of her tribe. If anything or anyone gets in the way of that (in the form of lack of money, loyalty, cooperation, integrity, etc.), things feel chaotic and threatened. If she has to do it herself, then she wants everyone to get out of the way. She prefers a team of equals and desires help.

She needs her man to have the courage to handle confrontation with centered wisdom, even if you are afraid of doing so. Bravery from you toward your sweetheart equates to safety, in her mind. Safe is what she'd like to feel this week. Stepping up as her hero who helps, rather than hurts, is what she wants. If you run and hide, or think in terms of yourself instead of the partnership and/or the family, she doesn't feel safe. She'll struggle this week to protect herself, her family, her future, and her happiness.

This is the week your woman simply needs to have her guy, her children, her co-workers, and her friends to have their own acts together. She depends on you to be rock solid, consistent, and tuned in as her closest ally and most dependable team member. She expects the week to function like a well-oiled machine, especially with her man.

Your sweetheart doesn't want to change the wonderful you. She wants to awaken your higher self because she likes living on a higher level. She wants YOU—the real you. She may believe in you more than you believe in yourself. Currently and collectively, women seem to be stepping into their higher selves at an accelerated pace, globally. We want our men to step up and be with us.

If you've participated in heart-to-heart talks during **Week 2, Winter**, and mind-to-mind talks during **Week 3, Spring** (after Ovulation is over with), then this is the place where you show that you've meant what you've said and have agreed to. If you find yourself in conflict with one another, my best suggestion is for *you* to be the one to acknowledge the issue and ask to table it until your heart-to-heart in **Week 2, Winter**. When that time comes, be sure the topic is discussed. She will love you for your desire to meet each other in understanding.

When we all learn to speak our truth from our hearts, it can only help us to strengthen our willingness to create a solid foundation of love, kindness, fun, and mutual respect.

Since she is so active mentally, and her body is beginning to feel uncomfortable, she may not be her most affectionate, nor is she likely to initiate sex. However, this does not mean she is not open to it; as a matter of fact, it may feel very good to her. But you must get it right.

Without any in-depth discussion about it, and without any expectations to go further on your part, simply test the waters.

As you work together using the 4s4w strategy, you'll become familiar with her signals, which will help you know what day she is on in her cycle. Hopefully, she'll be communicating this to you or using the 4s4w refrigerator magnets or some other support tool. Here are some questions to keep in mind:

- Has she already turned down sex but you're still looking for an opening?
- Is she initiating touch and indicating she'd like sex?
- Are you in the middle of a disagreement that has not yet been resolved?

If she's already said "no" to either your advances or an opportunity for sex, then take that as a "no." Just because she is saying no to sex doesn't mean she is saying no to *you*.

Respecting her desire to not participate in sex is a real turn-on for her, and your positive companionship will reflect this. It doesn't mean she'll change her mind, but it *does* mean that she is relieved that you *hear* her and that you'll be cool with being with each other in other ways. Her body is not cooperating and her mind is fixated on projects, but she *can* still enjoy her man being around and the good vibes between you. If you feel you MUST touch her, try giving her a foot or shoulder massage (if she likes them) without expecting anything more. Connected hugs and spooning while you sleep can often be a way to keep you physically and emotionally connected without the pressure of another person needing something from her. Attempt to clear up any arguments or bad feelings from the day before attempting to get physical. In general, I advise you to *not* relationship problem-solve at this time. Wait for **Week 2, Winter**.

If you push it after she has turned down the opportunity to have sex, you are saying that you either don't hear her or don't respect what she wants. She also doesn't want to be put in the position of turning you down. She doesn't like turning you down, ever, so instead, you may get an "okay" from an instantly infuriated woman. Not good.

If she indicates that she's open to sex, then be completely *willing* to get in tune with her vibe and her breathing. Go through each door slowly. Touch non-threatening places until you feel you have a green light to hit the spots. Is she responding or recoiling? Does she seem pleased and getting into the groove, or is she frowning and looking away? It really is this basic. This is the language she is speaking this week. Remember, she's in her head, not in her body. Her body is acting on its own, and it irritates her to have too much pawing going on. If you are a guy who wants to kiss all the time, back off and get out of her face if she looks annoyed. Focus on her responses in order to find the right path. The most important thing, however, is to talk with her during communication weeks two and three to find out exactly what she *does* like. Her likes and dislikes *are unique to her* and you will both benefit when you know them.

> **There is no wind that blows right for the sailor who doesn't know where the harbor is.** —Norwegian Proverb

Sex can be very good this week if you've got your partner's physical desires totally dialed in or if you're particularly good at reading when she is responding favorably or not. If you haven't developed these skills, be prepared for a possible rude awakening. She may get very blunt about it or want you to leave her alone. Chances are she has told you in the past what pleases her and what doesn't. Have you paid attention? In her mind, **Week 4, Summer** is *not* the week for more sexual or relationship training. This is the week when all the past communication you've done gets tested. Hopefully, she's been happily and lovingly discussing and sharing her knowledge of herself with you all month long in order for *you* to understand *her*, perhaps even getting specific about sexual technique preferences. She wants a connected relationship and hopes you will reciprocate with information about your own likes and dislikes.

This isn't the week to ask her to indulge you in a sexual favor. Her heart is in her "full-throttled" mind and her body is agitated. You don't want her to associate doing something sexual for you as a job, which is what can happen here. Again, pay attention. If she goes there on her own, then it is probably due to the good communication you two have been engaging in, and her stress is reducing each month.

Take the time to see this week as a positive chance to discover your misunderstandings, misperceptions, your own gifts to the world, and what you truly want in a relationship and out of life. It will be rewarding, I assure you. Be in your own complete power by taking responsibility for your participation in co-guiding your romantic union. Loving relationship facilitators Louis Corrosio and Trinity Harris teach that the key lies in *not* criticizing each other. Instead, express your underlying, true desires during your heart-to-hearts in **Week 2, Winter** and in your mind-to-minds in **Week 3, Spring**. I have found that attending weekend workshops for couples through-out the life of the relationship are a phenomenal way to keep the bond going.

In summary, stay at home to-gether, yet do your own things. This is a great chance for both of you to get projects done with focused efficiency. This is also a great time to bring home "take-out" food and reward yourselves with a movie that will make you laugh.

9. Challenging & Non-Cycling Rhythms

The most beautiful people I've known are those who have known trials, have known struggles, have known loss, and have found their way out of the depths.

—Elisabeth Kübler-Ross

Betrayal: When Our Feminine is a Bitch

L et's face it: our reproductive bodies betray us at times and we've no choice but to just deal with it.

It starts when we're young, forcing us to receive a legacy we neither asked for nor desired, invading our territory, or in this case, our favorite panties, with the bloodmark of womanhood. As apprehensive or fairly excited as we may be at first, the novelty of this rite-of-passage can wear off in a hurry, to be replaced by dread, resistance, or loathing.

Resigned to getting good at the art of this practice, we carry on with our contribution to the Greater Good month after month, with the promise that this investment will pay off with healthy children or some other unknown reward.

We discover that the journey is a rocky road at best. Cramps, mood swings, weight-gain, and self-doubt can *overwhelm* us, and radical pre-Period or perimenopausal symptoms can *destroy* us if we're not careful. Endometriosis, fibroids, estrogen dominance, cancer, long or uncooperative labors, lactation challenges, and fear of pregnancy (or no pregnancy) can make being a woman very difficult to be a human.

Holding One Another's Hands in Our Hearts

I am a Keeper of Stories. My life has been one of holding space for my friends when they are distraught and extending compassion or giving motherly/sisterly advice when needed. I have received the same in return. When I was a hairdresser in the early days of my working life, I discovered that there is great honor in hearing another's story and a responsibility that goes with it. While misuse of this information in the form of gossip or judgment is detrimental to all, the Keeper's job is to help heal the social structure by respectfully telling these stories when they serve a higher purpose. This interchangeable messenger position, Story Keeper to Story Teller, is shamanic in nature—medicine work. Teaching through stories is the oldest form of education and a vehicle toward justice. I believe that being this type of messenger is my position in society and my purpose in this lifetime in order to help steer our societal views toward equality for women. The stories that have been presented to me over the course of my life, and that I keep, are about the deeper, daily female experience. I am continually entrusted with stories of real life joys and trauma.

Our stories may be of pregnancy, birthing, cycles, hysterectomy, contraception, knowledge, sex, jobs, relationships, position, money, respect, abuse, body image, parenting, or sovereignty, but one thing is for sure: none of us are immune to the challenges of being female—from neither our reproductive bodies nor the global views of women. There are many mixed messages about the power that we are entitled to have over being female. Because of this, there is chaos within the collective core female essence; so much chaos, in fact, that we have become a gender divided.

Courage to Have Care and Compassion

The reproductive path is fraught with possibilities that can undermine our sense of self and femininity. The 4s4w system helps us to understand the wisdom of our natural feminine cycle when things are going well and gives us courage when our bodies or experiences are compromised. Knowledge about our core essence gives us hope and empowers us to maintain strength and dignity at the times when we need it most.

Our compassion, understanding, answers, trust, and unity lie in our gender stories. We must hear our own stories within that of one another's instead of criticizing, judging harshly, and voting to control what other women do. We all, ultimately, share the same struggles. We are one tribe, divided into the Pre-Bloods, the Blood Givers, and the Blood Keepers. No matter who we are or what culture we come from, we can do everything right to care for our reproductive bodies, minds, and spirits, and still have something go very wrong. Perhaps what we experience is simply unexpected or different from the other women in our lives. In this chapter I'd like to share some of these stories from sister journeyers, in their own words.

Perimenopause: When Enormous Changes Happen

By Jessica Vineyard

I was fortunate enough to have worked as a chemist at a compounding pharmacy when I started transitioning from a regular, predictable, monthly Period to a more erratic cycle. I was educating doctors and patients about symptoms of perimenopause and menopause and the benefits of bio-identical hormone replacement to ameliorate symptoms associated with them. Therefore, I was knowledgeable about what to do when my own symptoms started appearing.

They started with waking up throughout the night. I was always irritable. I felt constantly stressed, easily upset or angry, and took it out on everyone around me. Oddly, it took a while before I recognized these symptoms in myself as the very ones that I taught others to watch for! I thought it was everyone around me being stupid, irresponsible and argumentative. It took me a while to recall what I knew about hormonal changes. Once I put two and two together, I started on bio-identical progesterone and within days I was sleeping better, my anger diminished, and I felt "normal" again. I also had to do a lot of apologizing!

Perimenopause is the transition time between regular monthly cycles and menopause, the complete cessation of Periods. It can, and usually does, last for years. It can start any time between the late 30s and the mid-50s. Mine started when I was 38 and lasted until I was 45, when my menses stopped completely. It is a time of great changes in the female body.

Generally, progesterone is the first of the female hormones to start dropping off. This important "feel-good" hormone provides many positive benefits to the female body. It helps to regulate the sleep/wake cycle, prepares the body for pregnancy and is elevated throughout a pregnancy, provides a feeling of general well-being, and balances estrogen, among other things. When it starts to drop, often one of the first symptoms is waking up during the night. This may be followed by a general sense of feeling unwell, or not feeling like oneself. Since this hormone prepares the body for pregnancy every month, the diminishing production of progesterone also eventually causes the Period to become less predictable. Interestingly, Periods may start coming closer together at first. Eventually, as estrogen drops, they start coming less and less frequently, until they stop altogether and a woman enters menopause.

According to Christine L. Hitchcock, PhD research associate at the Centre for Menstrual Cycle and Ovulation Research (CeM-COR), University of British Columbia, Vancouver, perimenopausal women, particularly when in the early stages of transition, can often have higher-than-normal estradiol levels. She says research shows that "the process of perimenopause involves a breakdown in the feedback mechanisms that normally keep estradiol production in check." Consequently, ovulation can occur at times not considered typical, including during the Period itself. Because of this, it is crucial to use birth control throughout the month if pregnancy is not desired, as ovulation is too unpredictable to be accurately identified.

Some women experience no symptoms at all, and others may suffer severely. Night sweats, anxiety attacks, intense anger and rage, and loss of a sense of well-being are very common symptoms. Bio-identical hormones have been figurative and literal life-savers for women who suffer from them. While hormone replacement is not for everyone, it is certainly something to consider if you find that symptoms are disrupting your life. I received many, many phone calls and emails of gratitude from patients of the compounding pharmacy who wanted to let me know that their symptoms, and consequently their lives, were dramatically improved once they were able to balance their hormones.

There are now many practitioners who are well-versed in bio-identical hormone replacement. If you experience unbearable, or even just uncomfortable, effects during perimenopause, it might be well worth your time to discuss with your doctor the options available to you. It helped me, and thousands of other women, to transition more smoothly to our next phase of life.

PMDD and the Spiritual Menstrual Cycle

By Cat Stone Hawkins

I have been a sufferer of PMDD since my Periods started at the age of 13. I was unaware that it was my menstrual cycle that was causing problems, and I was deemed to be an unruly and out-of-control teenager. For many years, until the age of 27 when I was diagnosed, I had no idea I was suffering from the extreme form of PMS called Pre-Menstrual Dysphoric Disorder, PMDD.

PMDD affects a small number of women. It wrecks every aspect of their lives. Many women suffer physical symptoms such as painful cramps and sore breasts, but the most debilitating symptoms are the mental/emotional ones. Dysphoria brings up crazy, irrational thoughts. Far from being able to "get a grip" or "pull yourself together," sufferers feel like they are losing their minds. All normal perspective is lost. Feelings of being persecuted, paranoia, deep sadness, and anxiety will hit every month. There is also an overwhelming feeling of not being believed, as it is described by many as a Jekyll and Hyde illness. During the follicular phase it is possible to feel completely normal, cope with whatever life throws at you, and be kind and loving to your friends and family. During the luteal phase, it's like a demon is unleashed. It is almost impossible to control angry outbursts, desperate depression, anxiety, and fear. To date, there is no real treatment for PMDD and many women feel lost and alone. I have been on many medications over the years, none of which ever stopped the extreme mood swings.

I have spent my whole life delving into different aspects of the spiritual. I have always followed Nature/Goddess/Alternative paths. The one thing I could never completely embrace was my femininity.

To me, PMDD had caused me to hate being a woman. It made me despise the fact that I had a womb and had Periods, and I could relate to the old name given to menstruation, "The Curse." I felt I was cursed. I felt I would never be able to embrace the Feminine and truly love it the way I should. I have two children, both girls, and PMDD has made being a mother very difficult.

I found cycle awareness and the seasons of the cycle about a year ago. In that time, I have soaked up lots of information and delved into those places I was too scared to go. It was like a revelation. Being able to see my cycle in terms of the seasons of the year brought about a whole new dimension. I had a map! I had a baseline to compare myself to. With PMDD, it's very hard to distinguish what issues are being caused by the disorder, what are from outside influences or life issues, and what is from normal life stress.

By working with my cycle, embracing it, and understanding it, I feel I am much more in control of my PMDD. I have now begun to heal all of the things I criticized myself for. I am now completely medication- and birth control-free, which means I have nothing interfering with my natural cycle. I feel more in control and able to cope with life with PMDD. I plan my activities around my cycle, using each phase's strengths. I play when I feel good, I get things done when I'm in my "up" weeks, and I create, retreat, dream, and vision when I am in my "down" times. This has been my savior. Far from being a curse, it is a blessing. It has provided me with the knowledge to heal myself, and I have never felt better about being a woman. The menstrual cycle really is magical and a source of power for all women who choose to access it.

A QUESTION FROM SUZ TO CAT: The 4s4w system came to me as guidance and I put the sacred blueprint into action immediately. I followed it for seven or eight years, because it proved to be incredibly accurate, before it was suggested that I write about it. It wasn't my topic or specialty—I was just a woman who worked with a lot of other women and received this information spiritually. While researching my topic, I found author and midwife Jane Collings in Australia (with whom I connected and who was incredibly generous), and a blog by Christiane Northrup, M.D., both speaking of the four seasons and the female cycle. I stopped reading their stuff immediately to make sure my take on it was my own. I decided to keep writing because the women around me were not acquainted with this analogy. How were you first introduced to the concept of our feminine cycles corresponding to the seasons?

Cat: I first came across the concept while researching menstruation and spirituality. I came across the Moonsong website *www.moonsong.com.au/spiritualmenstruation.html* and then Alexandra Pope's book, *The Women's Quest*. It was like a light coming on and a "doh" moment of thinking, *WHY didn't I see that before and make that connection!* I then found Miranda Grey's books and website. This was at the beginning of 2011.

Suz: Thanks, Cat! I encourage everyone to check them out. It sounds like we're all speaking the same language, with various interpretations, just as our rhythm dictates.

(For more information on PMDD please visit Cat's blog at *www.meetmypmdd.blogspot.com*)

The Rough Road of Infertility: Teri's Story

By Teri Lux

After our marriage in 1991, my husband Bruce and I were excited about starting a family. When it didn't happen naturally after the first year, we looked into finding out why; this is how we entered the world of infertility testing.

I had a test performed, called a hysterosalpingogram, which showed I had severe blockage in both my fallopian tubes. In spite of our disappointment, we had hopes that a laparoscopy could correct the problem by clearing my tubes.

After the laparoscopy in 1993, we were devastated to discover that the scarring was too severe to be corrected, and my only hope of becoming pregnant would be through *in vitro* fertilization.

By this time my emotions were getting progressively more difficult to handle. My sisters and my sister-in-law all had their children, and several of our friends were starting their own families with ease.

While I shared in their happiness, I felt jealousy and self-pity as well, for which I felt ashamed. At times I felt like an incomplete woman.

These emotions contributed to our decision to pass on in vitro fertilization; we felt our chances were not good enough to warrant the financial and emotional investment. The possibility of another unsuccessful, and potentially devastating, experience was one I didn't think I could handle at that time.

We did believe we were assured of success in adopting a child who needed a home, however, and in 1995 we became foster parents to a wonderful two-year-old boy whom we were lucky enough to adopt.

In 2000, when our son had been an only child for five years, we decided that he really needed a sibling or two. As I began looking at adoption programs once again, Bruce said, "Why don't we see if we can get you pregnant this time?" Now I felt excited about that possibility and jumped on the Internet to research the options. We were excited to discover that success rates had improved with new technology that had been developed over the past seven years. We were also encouraged by financial options—especially a plan with a partial refund available if we weren't successful after three attempts. But most importantly, we were already happy with our family, so the idea of not being successful didn't seem nearly as devastating as it had before.

Before making a decision, however, we called Bruce's cousin, who lives in Michigan. We knew that he and his wife had struggled with infertility and had been through several rounds of *in vitro* procedures in two different states before finally becoming pregnant. When we asked where they had gone, we discovered their success occurred at the Pacific Fertility Center (*www.pfcla.com*), a Southern California facility—which is where we happen to live!

We made an appointment to meet with the doctor and, although I was 38 at the time, he was cautiously optimistic about our chances of success.

We signed up for the refund plan during our initial visit and were excited to leave with a detailed calendar for the following month, specifying the dates and times to administer the various medications. Although giving myself a daily injection wasn't exactly fun, I was really intrigued with the medical technology and totally excited about the possibility of success!

At the end of the month we returned to the Center to have the doctor check our egg production and were scheduled to return in a few days to have the egg retrieval performed. We were thrilled to learn that 21 eggs were retrieved to be fertilized! Three days after that we went back to see how many of the fertilized eggs had become viable embryos.

We had seven viable embryos and were then faced with the decision of how many to transfer to my uterus. The possibility of a multiple pregnancy of more than two or three babies was pretty scary—yet we knew that the more embryos transferred, the greater our chances of success.

Our doctor counseled us well. He told us that, due to my mature age, the chances of becoming pregnant with more than one or two babies were slim. Of course it was our decision to make, but he encouraged us to transfer all seven embryos, which we did.

Acknowledging that I would surely have felt diminishing enthusiasm with each successive attempt, we were overjoyed to get pregnant on our first try and, on October 13, 2000, I gave birth to twins—a girl and a boy.

When Hello Means Goodbye

By Christine Miller

My husband and I were thrilled to discover that I had gotten pregnant on our honeymoon in 1986. We decided that I would stay home for most of the pregnancy. That was a good thing, because I had terrible morning sickness, far beyond the typical first three months.

Throughout my pregnancy I was really excited. Smells really bothered me, but I ate well and took good care of myself. I live a healthy lifestyle, so I felt like I was doing all the right things. When I was about six months pregnant, I suddenly had a feeling that something was wrong; something inside me just knew it. I told my doctor, who reassured me everything was just fine.

I was due in December. After a 32-hour labor I gave birth to our little girl, Tiffany Christine. When she was born, she couldn't breathe. They immediately took her away from me. I didn't even get to hold her. I didn't know what was going on. It was a big blur of doctors and nurses running around.

When they finally brought her to me in an incubator, she was hooked up to all kinds of machines. She looked so beautiful, so perfect. But they told me there was something wrong. They were concerned about her head size, whatever that meant. They told me she was really sick. I finally learned that she had microcephaly, when water gets into the brain cavity before the brain is fully developed. It couldn't even tell her to breathe. They had to helicopter her to UC San Francisco. I couldn't go with her in the helicopter. And that was the last time I got to see her alive.

She died three days after she was born. As I left the hospital I was sitting there thinking, here I am going home, it's supposed to be a joyous time, but I have no baby. I was out of my body. People were asking, what did I have? Where is she? It was very painful, very traumatic. I didn't see myself in the mirror for four months after she died. I was in such grief, wondering what I had done wrong. I felt so sad, so guilty. Why was this happening to me when I was so careful? I must have done something wrong to deserve this. What did I do?

Time didn't really make things better, I just got better at living everyday life. But the pain and sadness are still as raw as the day my baby died. Suzanne was there with me throughout the whole experience. She was pregnant with her second child at the same time. I gave birth first, so it was really important to me, after a sad birth, to witness a healthy birth. Suzanne had her baby at home. I got to be there for that. It was very traumatic and emotional for me. I just kept thinking that her baby was going to be born and then die.

I wanted to get pregnant again right away but my body just wasn't ready. I did finally get pregnant again, and during that pregnancy I had to have multiple ultrasounds because the risk of having another child with microcephaly was doubled. In 1986 we were blessed with a 10-pound baby boy. Even after giving birth to a strong, healthy son, every time he cried I thought he was going to die.

Since we were newly married when I first got pregnant, my husband and I were just going through the transition of starting a life together. We became closer during our grieving. I believe that, out of everything bad that happens, there must be something good that comes out of it. As horrible as that time was to go through, I wouldn't change the experience at all. I was very lucky to have my husband to grieve with. I got to know him differently than how I may have, had we not had this experience. And we had a healthy baby boy; seeing our grown son as a successful, happy young man is everything to me. Most of all I learned about the fragility of life and how important it is to embrace every moment with loved ones.

Hysterectomy: A Letter to Suz

By Feather Gilmore

Note from Suzanne: Feather's story is a perfect example of someone finding her own unique interpretation of her weekly rhythms and how she relates them to the seasons, which differs from that presented in this book. I encourage you to do the same.

When I heard about your upcoming book, *4 Seasons in 4 Weeks*, it got me thinking about my own female experience. I am one of many women who live a "female-cycle-without-a-cycle" life.

In 1983, at the age of 28, I received what is called a total or complete hysterectomy or, the term that I think fits the situation best, a radical hysterectomy. A **radical** hysterectomy is the removal of the uterus, cervix, ovaries, and structures that support the uterus. When a woman undergoes a radical hysterectomy, surgical menopause follows immediately by bypassing the natural female processes that would have unfolded over time. So, instead of having years to experience both the gifts and the challenges of menses, perimenopause, and menopause, I was politely asked to adjust to my "change" immediately.

Surgery complete, I was sent home with a hysterectomy and without most of my female organs. Venturing forward by clearing my body from the fog of pain relievers, and painfully but successfully getting my first poop behind me (ha ha), I had proved to myself that not every precious organ was gone and that certain nerve endings had stayed intact.

Whew…so, everything's fine now. I'll sit around the house and rest for about four to six weeks and then it will be time to go back to my life, I thought. It would be nice if it had worked out that way. I may have recovered from the surgery but I was just beginning an unknown journey of changes—changes and cycles that I knew nothing about!

No one explained to me exactly what those changes would or could be. For years, a very big gap in knowledge, education, and understanding beckoned me to investigate. What little available information I found was sitting in the corner of allopathic textbooks and well-meaning practitioners' subtle trainings. Physically I was treated with menopause medications and given recommendations, but I was still a young woman and often felt like I had done something naughty. Maybe I had been sent to that particular medical corner not for comfort but for a "what will we do with you?" time-out. I couldn't find anyone who attended to the whole of my *female experience*.

I needed help. I wanted big-time, big-girl help! Without anyone coming to my cries for rescue, I jumped into the nearest phone booth (hard to find but still around) and kicked my superhero mind into high gear. I was to become my own sweet savior, in a spiritual sense. Holy Holistic Bat Girl! I was going to save my day!

Don your "how-to," "what-may-be," or "try-looking-at-it-this-way" superheroine outfit and then you will know how I had to deal with this body of emotions and conditions that was missing a physical form, but still called my belly "home." Although it took me years to find my way out of that phone booth, when I reentered the world I was geared up and glistening with insights and personal knowledge of the answers to the following questions:

    ∿ What is my understanding of the "hysterectomied female experience?"

    ∿ What does this circumstance do to the body, mind, sex, and soul of a woman?

    ∿ How do the experiences I encounter align with the events you speak about in your book, *4 Seasons in 4 Weeks*?

Enter our deeply connected friendship and all those long, insightful chats about being women, with all of our similarities and our uniqueness. Enter giving each other guidance and support. Enter your book.

Now that I have experienced walking the fine lines of femininity throughout my 20s, 30s, 40s, and into my 50s, without my female organs, yet with my biological female cycle still intact, I can genuinely advocate the value of your ideas, Suzanne.

A Barren Body Is Still Blessed

For over 25 years I have had the distinct pleasure of working with women in the realms of beauty, health and wellness. During my educational phases I was fortunate to have at my disposal access to current ideas, theories and research on women's health. The typical model that had served women's understanding of the purpose of their menstrual cycles, to notify us of Ovulation or pregnancy, broke down and through. Insightful men and women began to study how the female cycle was truly designed. They followed the biological, psychological, and spiritual lives of the female well-being experience. The keys were found, but for many women the doors still looked locked. We continued to be givers and nurturers of others, even when what we really needed was to care for ourselves.

Although I no longer have Nature's system to clue me in to how I might function and feel (hormonal changes), I do retain the natural signs and signals that can provide me with the keys to unlock my own doors. By paying close attention to my own flows and fluctuations of emotions, body sensations, and thoughts, the guidance and instruction on how to improve my experience and maximize my potential were there.

By exploring my own rhythms as being similar to your idea of the female cycle mirroring the seasons, I began to connect my cycling back to a more natural state. As the seasons in Nature each express their mysteries and responsibilities I, too, had mine. The natural wisdom encoded in the menstrual cycle of a woman was not lost to me just because I no longer had Periods. The blood flow ended but the female flow did not. The currents of my moods, memory, and magic were much deeper than just body and chemistry.

I have found that many women are similar in that they are interested in experiencing themselves through their relationships with others. On my journey of self-discovery, and perhaps due to the early hysterectomy and childlessness, I became aware that the relationship with my *self* was equally important. Let's agree to say that one of the essential purposes of a woman's menstrual cycle is a path for looking toward self. I believe it is. Ask most women to look closely and they will certainly see that, during their Periods, they are pulled toward noticing and (hopefully) attending to themselves, their needs, and desires.

I also have this "drawing in" toward self each month and it feels like the season of Winter to me. I find myself emotionally empty and somewhat lonely (remember, I'm already barren!). This time of the month used to feel like a stark place that re-enlivened wounds, like scar tissue stretching over bone. I was acutely aware of my body, size, weight, and worries, and just wanted to curl up and hibernate. Maturing has brought with it a different sense. No longer is my own body inhospitable, and I don't feel deserted. Empty, yes. But it is now an open place, an *opportunity* requiring minutes and moments of self-reflection, an open space of opportunity for rest and relaxation. Now is the week to nurture myself through activities that color my spirit or soothe my soul, with tears of release from held emotions from previous weeks.

Letting go is the way of Winter, letting go of what has gone before and then connecting with what is left, the bare bones of me. I can be a bit cold in tone and temperament as I snuggle up inside my inner landscape, so I watch my words. This is the week that I extend my directness to whoever is in my igloo. Honesty is there but I'm pretty self-contained so it's best not to question me; I might just tell you way more than you want to hear!

After my time alone inside I find an emerging, a desire to share the vitality I just recently renewed. This reminds me of the season of Spring. In springtime Nature is definitely a busy bee and I find myself buzzing, too. Although I take estrogen on a daily basis, it seems to kick in or harmonize with the elements of renewal, and my body feels refreshed and wanting physical release. Give me your tired, your hungry, your…whatever. In other words, I'm ready to produce, organize, deliver, and stand on the soapbox! I'm as open as the flower beginning to bloom. I seem to know exactly what I need and what I should and can do.

This week is my super-star, sexy, and sassy week. I really want to be seen and taken home to bed. My body and brains are happy and beautiful and the only caution is that I'm so sensuous that I may lose some of my sense-making, so I will take care with my engaging and be careful not to say "yes" to everything. Maturing has gifted me some wisdom here, so that I can remember that there are other weeks and other experiences coming. I will fly high in this season of power and opportunities, but with insight of the mountains up ahead.

And the mountains do rise up, but what goes up must come down. Down I go into my third week. I have just landed into the season of Summer's warmth and a down-in-the-valley period. All I desire now is some rest from flying high and happy. I'm a bit warm and worn out from all that productivity. Sleepy, hungry, and thirsty, with days of falling moods, I want to sedate in body, mind, and spirit. This is the week you will find me juicing and eating every color in the rainbow. As I rally my nutritional practices, I will usually be rejecting my partner's sexual advances. Give me my women friends! They are the perfect company to slow-walk with me into places and spaces that occupy my mind and body now. Conversations are in…cuddling is out!

My dog-days of summertime used to leave me drained but, having matured through this process of knowing my cycles, I can use the downtime and yet remain focused and organized, enjoying the previous expenditure of energy, remembering that soon enough another season will change and so will I.

Fall has arrived. It is a time, a season, a week, within my monthly cycle that holds endings, beginnings, and all the in-betweens. Just as Fall weather can be cold and overcast in the morning and by late afternoon be sunny and warm, I am a combination of elements and expressions. If I have been alert and attentive, accepting and allowing during all the other weeks (seasons), then I am prepared for the potential ups and downs that I may now feel.

With the wisdom of balancing practices throughout the weeks of Winter, Spring, and Summer, when I am Fall I am beautiful. When I feel like falling down or apart, drifting into depression or denial, I can still be beautiful. In the past this was the most difficult phase of my female cycle—unpredictable, stress-filled, odd and imbalanced. Anger could flare up as red as the turning leaves and then leave me hanging, suspended by only a thin membrane, twirling in the wind and falling at any given moment.

Views and perceptions hover under a cloud of doubt if I forget the wisdom of my now-seasoned self. This week is not my best time to make decisions that are life changing, like ending a job, or redecorating a room, or even trying a new hair color. If I lose touch with my compassionate side, then I can become critical and self-defeating, as if the reduction in the sunlight also minimizes my light and brightness.

Without a clear reflection of my spiritual self, the week of Fall can overturn my confidence. Staying with practices that ground me in stability and keep my rooted senses safe allows me to stay stable as this time of upheaval blows by. Moving in directions with patience and love is the lesson of this weekly season.

Suzanne, we have been friends for many seasons, moving in and out of life's sweet Spring blooms, and have kept each other warm during stark Winters of loss and fragility. We have sweated out Summers of life challenges and kept ourselves standing firm in the unpredictable Falls of maturing. Woman to woman, my female experience has been enhanced by your light, laughter, and love.

Menopause: A New Beginning

By Louise Abel Curtis

Stedman's 27th Edition Medical Dictionary defines menopause as "permanent cessation of the menses; termination of the menstrual life."

This is not the most descriptive nor profound explanation of a process that, for many women, will last up to ten years and turn their lives upside down with serious physical symptoms and emotional upheaval. If one Googles the word "menopause," over ten million results emerge, with promised "cures" ranging from hormone replacement to miracle substances and surgical procedures. This illustrates not only the interest level regarding this subject, but also the need for accurate information in order to reach beyond medical terminology and mere myth.

Menopause is often called the "change of life" and is a naturally occurring process in a woman's life, when the cycle of menstruation ends. Contrary to the beliefs of the past, menopause is not an "illness"—mental or physical. It is a demarcation of sorts, dividing the time between a woman's reproductive, childbearing years and that which is now called the "third age." This third age is a time that reaches far beyond that of the end of menstruation—it can be the beginning of a rewarding journey that may prove to be transformational at the very least.

Menopause is a physiological process, a natural end to the reproductive cycle. It includes the cessation of the working life of the ovaries. Generally, menopause is considered complete after 12 consecutive months with no menstruation. The 13th month is the beginning of the postmenopausal era.

For most women, menopause usually occurs between the ages of 45 and 55, but it can occur as early as 40 and as late as 60. This transition is in no way a 12-month process; it can last anywhere from one to 10 years. Symptoms often include hot flashes, night sweats, insomnia, migraines, vaginal dryness, urinary frequency and urgency, joint and muscle pain, development of osteoporosis, breast tenderness and swelling, decreased elasticity of the skin, irritability, fatigue, memory loss, depression, anxiety, decreased libido, and painful intercourse, just to name a few!

These symptoms and effects can be experienced in various combinations over a short or long period of time. Some women may have no symptoms at all, while others have a long, difficult time. It has been found that, in some cases, those who consider menopause a medical malady have a more negative experience than those who view it as a transitional phase in their lives.

As individual as all women are, the process of menopause can be as varied as women are unique. It is at times a most difficult experience, one fraught with pitfalls, but can also be a valuable contributor to an individual's personal growth.

My own story is one of drastic change. It may be similar in many ways, or it may be different, when compared to the stories of our daughters, our sisters, our mothers, and our grandmothers. I only hope that it brings the reader valuable insight into her own experience.

On December 24, 1994, after a lovely holiday dinner with my family, I fell suddenly and violently ill. I spent most of that night nauseated, vomiting, and dizzy. I developed a high fever and abdominal cramps; a somewhat "normal" Period had become hemorrhagic… not a very happy holiday!

That was the last (and most memorable) time that I menstruated. I was 44 years old and had had my Period since age 11. And, although menstruation had ceased, I was in no way finished with what has been called by many "the curse." For the next several years I was plagued with insomnia and night sweats; days were full of hot flashes, anxiety attacks, and depression. I gained over 60 pounds.

Not every woman has the severe symptoms that I did. And although my symptoms seemed at times impossible to endure, I chose (after much pondering and research) not to use hormone replacement therapy (HRT) to ease the symptoms and postpone the inevitable. Instead, I used alternative therapies to see me through. These included homeopathic and naturopathic remedies, vitamins, minerals, and herbal supplements. The one allopathic treatment I agreed to was an antidepressant, which I took for only one year.

This was prescribed in order to achieve some sense of balance to my emotions so that I could begin a program of weekly counseling and therapy.

As my emotions became more balanced, I embarked on a more intense and rigorous writing routine, including dream journaling. I also began more in-depth work in the visual arts, including drawing, painting, and especially collage, which assisted in my "process" work as an adjunct to therapy. Although some of the physical symptoms persisted for many years, the emotional and psychological work I did kept me afloat, and I was able to find deeper meanings in the roller coaster transitions of my life.

During these years of change I survived a difficult divorce, moved to a house of my own, and started a new life. This was a time for digging deep into my psyche, peeling back the layers and discovering who I really was and who I wanted to become.

In conjunction with therapy, I began a program entitled "The Artist's Way" by Julia Cameron. This program is not just for artists—it is for everyone. It guided me in the search for my authentic self; it assisted me in examining childhood trauma, family issues, and life-changing events, which contributed to a better understanding of my life and my past. It gave me the tools to continue evolving into a new being. It encouraged a daily writing habit that has been crucial to my continued growth.

This was a time to take care of myself, to put myself first on my own to-do list, for the first time in my life. I began a regular program of exercise (including martial arts, yoga, dance, and weight training), meditation, and a healthy eating regimen. I lost the weight I had gained.

My menopause lasted approximately 10 years, which sounds daunting. However, the first three or four years were the most intense, and subsequently many of the symptoms gradually tapered off, with some disappearing entirely (including the anxiety and depression). Some of these symptoms, including mild hot flashes, cravings, insomnia, and fatigue, began to fluctuate with the Moon—Full and New—as if I were still cycling.

This cycling continues today and, since I have been focused on myself and fulfilling my own needs, I actually feel more connected to family, friends, and others, and to the cycles in my life. In essence, I feel more connected to daily rhythms, seasonal changes, the elements, to the ebb and flow of the Moon and tides, to myth and ritual, and especially to my own energies, creative, spiritual, emotional, and physical, in a renewed and natural way.

I finally reached a phase in this process when I felt healthier and more balanced physically, mentally, and emotionally. Then I was able to ask myself the following questions:

- What do I want to do with my time now?
- How can I know myself better?
- How can I live an authentic life?
- What would I like to learn?
- How do I balance all aspects of my life?
- How do I reevaluate my values?
- What do I want to become?

The answers were surprising, but they led me on a path to a new life and a new self. I continue to periodically ask myself these questions, and the answers demonstrate how far I have come as I mark the many milestones on this journey.

In this way my life has changed. And it has changed for the better. My priority now is the continuing evolution of my self. I base my life around activities I love: writing, drawing, painting, collaging, dancing, martial arts, and traveling on the path of continued self-discovery. It can be an arduous journey, but one that is worth every minute and every drop of those night sweats!

Now I can truly interpret the phrase "change of life" as not an ending, but as a beginning—the beginning of a new and better self, as a wiser, freer, more creative, and authentic woman. I can only wish all women the same.

4s4w Ceremonial Aspects

Season	Fall	Winter	Spring	Summer
Sensory	Sound Intuition	Sight Touch	Smell Taste	All Senses
Element	Earth	Air	Water	Fire
Direction	West	North	East	South
Planet	Mercury	Saturn	Neptune	Mars
Color	Deep Red	Blue	Green	Rose
Chakras	Root 1 3rd Eye 6 Heart 4	Heart 4 /Throat 5 Sexual 2 Power 3	Sexual 2 Crown 7 Power 3/Throat 5	Power 3 Root 1 3rd Eye 6
Flower/Herb	Lavender	Sage	Violet	Rosemary
Attribute	Inspiration	Communication	Manifestation	Healing
Astrological	Aquarius Gemini Libra	Capricorn Taurus Virgo	Pisces Cancer Scorpio	Aries Leo Sagittarius
Oil /Incense	Sandalwood	Pine	Myrrh	Frankincense

Ovulation

2 4 6 8 10 12 14 16 18 20 22 24 26 28

ABonsall

4s4w Correspondence

Season	Fall	Winter	Spring	Summer
Cycle	Period	"Venus"	Ovulation	Fire Walk
Moon Phase	New Moon	Waxing Moon	Full Moon	Waning Moon
Symbolism	Shedding	Becoming	Expressing	Exploring
Hormones	Resting Est/Pro Low	Rising Estrogen	Maintaining Est - / Pro+	Dropping All Drop
Libido	Relaxed Sweet	Seductive Intoxicating	Primal/Spiritual Sacred	Quick Release Smoothing
Energy	Low	Building	High	High to Low
Attitude	Resigned Hopeful	Flirty Heartfelt	Powerful Encompassing	Edgy Exasperated
Mind Mood	Creative	Motivated	Brillant	Sharp
Archetypes	Queen Visionary Artist	Builder Fun Date Lover	Goddess Wise Women World Leader	Athlete Fire Walker Monk

Ovulation

2 4 6 8 10 12 14 16 18 20 22 24 26 28

ABonsall

4s4w Archetypes

Week	Season	Moon	Archetype	In State of...	What Action to Take
1	Fall	New	Queen	Self-care	Rest / Release
			Visionary	Reception	Receive
			Artist	Creation	Rejuvenate
2	Winter	Waxing	Builder	Manifesting	Become
			Fun Date	Caring	Connect
			Lover	Attraction	Seduce
Ovulation					
3	Spring	Full	Goddess	Full Expression	Enjoy
			Wise Woman	Reflection	Advise
			World Leader	Governance	Lead
4	Summer	Waning	Athlete	Competition	Exercise
			Fire Walker	Discovery / Observation	Overcome
			Monk	World Peace	Be at Peace

ABonsall

Women's Work

10. Daily Rhythms

Deciphering Your Personal 4s4w Code

Nothing ever becomes real 'til it is experienced.
—Keats

Be Your Own Expert

I can't be the expert on *your* cycle experience—only you can be. I'm asking you to tap in, turn on, and take charge. New findings about hormones are being uncovered daily and professional opinions vary about their meaning. The field has become very exciting, with more and more doctors keeping up on the latest information. Understanding and balancing our hormones not only shows us how to feel better now, but it helps us to comprehend the importance they play in preventing diseases such as Alzheimer's from devastating our future.

The one thing that has *not* changed is the female *experience*, and this is where you come in. Not only can understanding your hormonal rhythm help you make better health, lifestyle, and relationship decisions, but with this understanding you are personally contributing to scientific research and even to the global understanding of how women function. You will begin to see how important it is that you make your views known in the world. By tracking your *experience* of your cyclic rhythm, and then bringing this information to your health practitioner, you join other women in the first line of defense against illness.

When you implement the 4s4w strategy you'll be prepared with more information when you go to your annual exam. This will eliminate some of the guesswork. The doctor can't help you as much if you can't answer questions about yourself. YOU are the only person who can be an expert on YOUR day-to-day *experience*, which allows the physician to be the expert on translating what the hormones are doing. Take charge of your health because, in the long run, no one is keeping track of it the way you can. I can't be the expert on your cycle experience—only you can be. I'm asking you to tap in, turn on, and take charge.

Women's Work: Implementing 4s4w

The beauty behind 4s4w is that you do not need to go the distance to be successful. If you do nothing more than read this book, I guarantee you will never look at your cycle in the same way again. You may find this to be enough to improve your female *recycling* experience because you will begin to be more attentive, more present.

The deeper you go with this system by tracking your cycle and then studying it, the more knowledgeable you'll be about YOU and your body, mind, and spirit health.

Implementing means to:

◔ Track daily

◔ Be attentive

◔ Know where you are at in your cycle by looking at your chart

◔ Identify the significance and characteristics of your cycle until you become familiar with the signs

◔ Make mindful decisions

◔ Plan ahead

◔ Communicate with your partner

One Size Does NOT Fit All

You are unique! The 4s4w method is meant to be a guideline—an easy way to manage your cyclic and rhythmic female body. What is specific for me will not necessarily be specific for you. No one else, not even your doctor, is able to fine-tune your system the way that you can. Of course, your physician can assist you in your quest for maintaining good health, but ultimately you are the only one who can be in charge of *you* 24/7.

You are a real live woman, not a chart on paper. Everyone is a little different, so only *you* will be able to track your cycle to begin to get your patterns down. My **Spring** week has been adjusted—it begins on Day 12 instead of Day 15, which also causes my **Fall** and **Winter** weeks to adjust. As you get the basics down, you'll be able to take these analogies and make these "season" weeks longer or shorter. Be attentive to your needs and this guidance will prepare your body for an exquisite internal adventure, month after month.

The Workshop in the Basement

It is very difficult to understand yourself when so many things are happening in your body that you are not aware of. Basically, your hormonal system is like having Santa's workshop in the basement of your house. If you know about it, then you know what to expect and what the routine is. If you don't know what is going on in your basement, or you're barely aware that you have a basement, then the pounding hammers are going to keep you wondering if you're a little crazy, and the smell of paint is going to make you feel sick. Your body, mind, and spirit are yours to manage, so it is vital to know what is going on in your own personal temple day to day.

Do the First Step Only, or Go the Distance

I have given you the information as I understand it. The rest is up to you to apply and customize for yourself. Do the first step only, or go the distance.

❧ Step One

- •**Read** and reread about the four weekly seasons. Do they resonate with you? Why or why not? Are you beginning to think about your cycle differently?
- •**Comprehend** the basics of what your hormones are doing, biologically.
- •**Consider** what your cycle represents, how it changes daily, and its effects on you.
- •**What do you think** it is doing right this minute?

❧ Step Two

- •**Track** your own cycle for a few months using the 4s4w Tracking Chart or phone app. Be sure to do this every night.

❧ Step Three

- •**Discover** how the four weekly seasons surface and reveal themselves.

∿ Step Four

- **Notice** what *your* regular, unique rhythm looks like.

- **Replace** my 4s4w characteristics descriptions with your own experiences as needed.

∿ Step Five

- **Plan** ahead. Begin to tag your calendar or phone app with your four seasons a month *ahead* of time. Create memos or reminders for yourself throughout each of these weeks (i.e., heart-to-heart talks this week!).

∿ Step Six

- **Implement** mindful choices.

- **Adjust** the number of days in each of your seasonal weeks where necessary (i.e., **Week One, Fall**: six days instead of seven).

∿ Step Seven

- **Congratulate** yourself for tuning into YOU! Now keep it going!

She Who Walks with the Moon: Tracking without a Period

Remember, our female bodies are wired with this cyclical rhythm from the time we are born until the time we die, and surfaces during our reproductive years to show us the wisdom of this amazing blueprint! Even if you've experienced menopause or a hysterectomy, your body is still female and remembers your rhythm just fine.

If you are a Blood Keeper (not bleeding anymore), I suggest you track with the Moon phases, beginning with the New Moon, to see if you follow its energy sequence. Follow the symbolism of the 4s4w guidance. Keep up this tracking—the more you do it, the more attentive you'll be to uncovering your true fundamental nature, your own feminine secrets.

Month		Week 1, Fall	Week 2, Winter	Week 3, Spring	Week 4, Summer
Cyclers: Begin at Period		Period	Venus Week	Ovulation	Fire Walk
Non-Cyclers: Begin at New Moon		New Moon	Waxing Gibbous Moon	Full Moon	Waning Crescent Moon
		Rest/Vision	Become/Seduce	Fully Express	Observe/Transform
		Internal	External	External	Internal

Date																															
Day #	1	2	3	4	5	6	7	8	9	10	11	12	13	14	15	16	17	18	19	20	21	22	23	24	25	26	27	28	29	30	31
Low – Med O High +																															
Overall Health – O +																															
Energy — O +																															
Libido — O +																															
Mind Mood — O +																															
Sleep — O +																															
Communication – O +																															
Contraception																															
Sex																															
Exercise																															
Good nutrition																															
Beauty/Self-care 1–10																															
Feeling the Love 1–10																															
Indicators																															
Headache																															
Acne																															
Cramps 1–10 scale																															
Breast Tenderness																															
Irritability																															
Depression																															
"Hot Spots"–Week 4																															

Tracking Your Cycle, Day by Day

Tracking is EASY!

1) Use the Tracking Chart and Instructions in this book

   a. Download the Tracking Chart to the left at **www.4seasons4weeks.com**.

2) Use the *4s4w Daily Tracker and Journal*

   a. This separate booklet contains monthly, weekly, and daily trackers and journal. See the back page of this book for how to order one.

3) Use the 4s4w Phone App

Tracking Chart Instructions

Remember, this is YOUR chart! Customize it for you. You can also create your own chart, if you'd like. Do whatever serves your needs the most. The idea is to get in tune with your monthly rhythm by tracking every single day. The more you do, the better you'll get at it.

1) Choose the best time of the day to fill out the chart and do your best to be consistent with this. If you choose morning, you'll be documenting how you feel upon arising. If you choose night-time, you'll be charting how you felt during the day. You could even choose to have two copies going at once, one for morning and one for nighttime.

2) If you are still having a Period, please begin this chart on the first day of your Period.* If you no longer bleed, then I suggest beginning Day 1 on the actual New Moon. Adjust as you become familiar with your cycle.

3) Fill in Month

4) Fill in "Date" with the day of the month. For instance, if your

Period, Day 1, begins on Sept 7th, begin filling in the boxes as 7, 8, 9, and so on.

5) All Categories: Make a simple mark to signify how you're feeling. For instance, if your overall health is great that day, mark a "+" for great. Plus (+), minus (-), and O indicate positive, negative, and neutral.

6) Mind Mood: This covers a general feeling about your mental/emotional outlook and self-esteem.

7) Contraception: Mark an "X" to indicate that you've taken a birth control pill or used contraception that day.

8) Indicators: This is a list of common challenges or accomplishments that you may want to track. Mark an "X" on a particular day when one of these applies. Use this list or delete the words and create your own.

9) Tracking for three months or more will give you a better understanding of your rhythm.

*A Note About Finding Your Marker Days

- The first day of Week 1, Fall is always the first day of your Period. If you easily spot (bleed a little here and there), count Day 1 as the day that you are getting the real deal—the day your blood is flowing red all day.

- The first day of Week 3, Spring is always Ovulation in the 4s4w strategy. Identifying Ovulation may take you a while to get good at, but eventually you'll get there. You'll be guesstimating most of the time unless you use one or more of the following:

  o An Ovulation kit, which can be ordered online and used at home.

  o An online Ovulation calculator. These are useful for getting an idea of when you can expect to ovulate. HOWEVER, these are not unique to your particular body or emotional influences, which can alter your cycle. Use this for educational purposes only, not for your personal accuracy.

o Follow and document your cervical mucus and temperature. Take a class in a Fertility Awareness Method.

o Search online for the latest methods. There are many sites and books to show you how to do this. They are often marketed toward predicting fertility.

o Make notes on the chart about how you're feeling. Include any changes in your thought processes, as this is an enormous clue for identifying the phase you are in.

Keep the Balance: Reminders

You are not sick: Your cycle is completely natural, and there is no need to stop doing the things you love or the things you are responsible for doing during the resting phases. Understanding your cycle is about being mindful. There is no need to share your cycle information with the people around you unless you want to, other than your sexual partner. It's up to *you* to make decisions about how you are handling things.

Don't forget that you are rhythmic: Once you've tracked a few cycles and put 4s4w into action, it is vital that you don't fall back into old patterns by forgetting that you are rhythmic. Just because you're feeling good now doesn't mean you can go back to burning the candle at both ends. Keep an eye on the bigger picture, rather than how you feel at the moment, and you'll keep the balance. Each day changes slightly, and each week overlaps with the other, merging into the next.

It's all about prevention: Remember, the decisions you make today will affect how you will feel tomorrow and even much further down the road. Honoring your rhythm *now* is the most powerful preventative medicine you can choose.

The purpose of following 4s4w is to bring your rhythm to the surface, noticing the perceived positives and negatives in order to identify them easily when they come around again month after month. Continue to re-read the sections on the four weekly seasons to help you attune to your own patterns.

Tracking Your Cycle, Month by Month

Month One: Track your cycle. Make notes regarding your mind, body, and soul. Use the *4s4w Daily Tracker and Journal*.

Month Two: Begin to incorporate 4s4w. Re-read the sections about each week as you enter into it. Pay close attention to its advice. Incorporate your guy whenever you're ready to share information. See if he is willing to participant by understanding his role.

Month Three: Begin to think about how each week has a beginning, a middle, and an end. For instance, Winter week begins *after* your Period. Your juices will be drier at that time, but by the end of Winter week, you'll be very wet. With Spring week, you'll start out very sexual, but after Ovulation, your sexuality will take on a new form and continue to morph in beautiful ways.

Month Four: Start to blend the weeks together by planning for Summer week during the second half of Spring week. Know that what you do now will affect how you feel in a few days. This is where real change begins to happen. You must always be planning ahead for the following season. If you want to feel better during Summer week, the Fire Walk, then begin making great decisions toward that goal during Spring week. A great female recycling experience can be easily attained with mindfulness.

Month Five: Now you're beginning to sync with your rhythm. It's time to be proud of noticing your patterns and the decisions you are making about them.

Month Six: Fine-tune the process. Practice makes perfect, yet keep in mind that this rhythm of yours is like a flowing river. The river course doesn't change, but the currents and water levels do. Navigating your cycle is very much like river rafting. The more you go down the same river, the more you know what twists and turns to expect up ahead, and can more easily address the changing conditions.

Repeat: Continue tracking for the duration that suits you. I've been tracking my cycle since 1988 because I absolutely love it.

The Importance of Paying Attention Now

by Jeanne Normand White, MSOM, L.Ac.

Each month we have the opportunity to re-evaluate, reflect, tune in to, purge, etc., to see what corrections need to be made. It can change the course of our lives to where we need to be.

I think the monthly cycle prepares us for the greatness we receive (empowerment, wisdom, enlightenment) when we go through menopause. If the work isn't done while we are still bleeding, it's a tragedy and missed opportunity. Often women who haven't done this work—ignored or medicated during the mood cycle—haven't made the course corrections in their lives and have lived and settled with bad decisions, relationships, and ways of being, etc. They feel lost, confused, and depressed, during and after menopause. Some women become extremely angry, sad, and/or suicidal when they enter menopause. I think it's because they realize that they missed their opportunity to live the life they were really hoping for. We become enlightened about our lives in menopause and what a hard realization it is to have—"If only I had . . . "

Our cycles are there to show us what needs to be changed in our lives. It could be some long-standing pattern that is not serving us any longer, still feeding into the drama of our lives. It could be an intimate relationship or a friend who isn't benefiting, but actually harming, us spiritually. It could be a job or house, etc. We are so lucky as women to have this monthly Moon that helps reflect back to us what is working and not working in our lives.

Conclusion

A bird doesn't sing because it has an answer,
it sings because it has a song.
—Maya Angelou

Myan's Story

When I was pregnant with my last child, I had one recurring vision. I began to notice it would come to me when I was out on a walk with my dog Ginger, a gentle, older white Samoyed whom we had adopted when her owner moved out of the country. As we both moved along in our cumbersome bodies, lost in the smell of our Oregon surroundings and refreshing Winter breeze, I would, all of a sudden, find myself in a most curious state— something I had never experienced before, pregnant or not: a state of *being*. I was at One with my natural environment and the Universe; I was at One with Spirit. Perhaps it is what others experience as "bliss." For a split second, it felt as if I was in the calm eye of a storm. More than anything, I remember feeling in sync with the swaying trees— that I actually *understood* them and was one of them. It was then that *she* would appear.

It was a vision of a young woman with curly, auburn hair. Who was she? Was this my soon-to-be daughter? How strange that my mind did not conjure up a baby or a little girl! Did this mean she was an "old soul?" Just as quickly as she appeared, she vanished, along with my connection to everything around me. When it happened again I tried to make it last longer, but the noticing and the questioning would pull me out of it every time.

Pregnant women can get obsessive about certain things with certain pregnancies. This time around for me, it was the baby's name. For whatever reason, I got stuck on "M" names. If she was born anywhere in the vicinity of her due date, March 8th, she would be a Pisces, so I determined that she must have a "water" name. Finding a water name that began with "M" proved to be a challenge. My husband and I were not finding a name we could both agree on. I decided this kid might have to name herself. I'm pretty sure *that* is exactly what happened.

My belly and I made a trip to visit my cousin Doreen in Birmingham, Alabama. As we stood talking in the kitchen of her big, beautiful home, a little t.v. sat off to the side with CNN Headline News revolving every thirty minutes. We weren't paying attention until something caught my eye. "…and this is the hot new model from Israel. Her name is *Mayaynn*, and it means 'water from the spring.'" I observed that she was a very natural-looking young woman with curly auburn hair. They even spelled her name, which had a lot of Ys and Ns, but I was so shocked that I couldn't retain it, except that it sounded like Mayan.

I relayed my vision to Doreen, so we waited for the next round of repeated news stories. There she was again. Mayan. Hmm. I wasn't sure. It wasn't an easy name for Americans; it sounded like the tribe of people with the same name, or it could get confused with "Maya," and I knew for sure that my husband would not like it. But I called him that night anyway with the story, and he *did* like it, and the name stuck. We decided to spell it like Ryan, for simplicity. The baby in utero from then on was "Myan." It seemed to fit.

I'm not Jewish, but when I got home I contacted our local rabbi, David Zaslow, and asked him about the name. He looked into it and found that it was considered an Israeli desert name meaning "source of spring water"—an offshoot of *mayim*; water. I visualized an oasis— a safe haven of beauty and restoration of health—a place where everyone is welcomed and loved, a place where their thirst is quenched. I loved it.

When I went back to work, one of my clients, Jennifer, asked me if we had a name picked out. When I told her the baby's name and what it meant, she freaked out. "You know what that means, don't you? 'Water from the spring?'" She was a phenomenal artisan, a potter who I was just then learning had had an "experience," and who was just then in the process of writing a book, from divine guidance, on female sacred wisdom.

She explained that the mythical Guinevere represented the Sacred Feminine, during a time when women were held in high esteem and in equal power with men. The women were the Keepers of the Well Water, water from the source of the planet, spring water coming from the womb of Mother Earth.

As the story goes, Guinevere and her maidens stood by the well and handed out cups of water to the soldiers who were passing through. One day darkness came. The soldiers took advantage of Guinevere and the maidens, raping them and pillaging the well, taking control of the sacred spring water that only the Keepers were allowed to touch and manage. This, Jennifer said, was the symbolic story for the beginning of Patriarchy—an attempt to have control over the womb, control over creation, and control over the sacred core wisdom of women.

Jennifer saw the impending birth of my child as a sign—a sign that, indeed, the Sacred Feminine, the spring water, was returning after a very long imprisonment to claim what was rightfully hers, to stand in her place of royalty once again.

The Feminine applications were turned off, so to speak, and the whole system is coming back online now. Reclaim what is natural for you—the hunger that has been inside of you the whole time.

I see my daughter Myan, who was, naturally, born right in the center of her due date (which just happens to be International Women's Day), as a representative of her generation who has come to show us how to provide beauty, safety, and restoration of health to the planet, the Balancer who is needed to harmonize male and female energies, to once again align Nature with Spirit so that the universal forces may come together in Love.

The female has arrived

Epilogue

The Rhythmically Intelligent Blueprint

While it is natural for many women to want children, this is simply *one* of many primal baselines that shows us what it is we contribute to the world—a microcosm of greater possibilities and true beauty. We birth new projects and nurture them to fruition on a regular basis. We teach and guide those around us. We continually show up and offer our medicine when we hear a cry of distress. Within our own four walls shines an organized boss, a fiscal manager, an overall visionary, and an intuitive *empath* who carries with her the psychological and emotional needs of each member of her immediate family and community circles. We are sensuously luscious and attentive. We are common-sense problem-solvers and no-nonsense leaders who can leap into action or a minivan faster than you can say, "Get your shoes on and grab your coat."

No matter what our ages, whether we are creating a bustling home environment or running a Fortune 500 company, liberal or conservative, with or without children, we are hard-wired as females to innovate, create, produce, lead, motivate, transform, rearrange, satisfy, and beautify. We are lunar-rhythmic beings, and the hormonal journey we each travel teaches us how to use this well-rounded intelligence and skill every month, *whether we listen to it or not*. Every female meets her Moon at adolescence, but it is not until she taps into conscious synchronization with her own phenomenal, cyclical rhythm that she steps into and aligns with her womanhood. *This* is our most important rite of passage—the homecoming into self-appreciation, rightful purpose, maturity, and satisfaction that is offered to each of us.

Like sleeping in our own cozy beds after being on the road for too long, it is here where we relax into the bliss of our individual natures. It is here where we take comfort in our own abilities to love and accept ourselves as the heroines of our own life stories. It is here where we luxuriate in the scars and fleshiness of our own bodies and become excited about and familiar with the inner workings of our creativity and our brilliant minds. It is here where we belong and fit in to the always-connected glistening web of sisters, past, present, and future, which lives peacefully intertwined with the strong web of mature brothers. It is here where the struggle ends and the thriving begins. It is here where we find our courage waiting for us to pick it up, put it on, and stand tall when presenting our unique gifts to the world. It is here where we know exactly what to do to relieve suffering in the world and then take action to do so. When women thrive, the world thrives.

Each willing woman is being called on to remember and recognize the ancient wisdom within her— the timeless message in a bottle. When we are attentive to the seasons within our own Moon cycles and the guidance each week provides, we not only discover our own Authentic Female, we connect to the Authentic in others, the needs of the planet, and the greater forces of the Universe. Within this rhythmic core resides the true power, wisdom, and beauty of every woman's nature.

Endnotes

1. Rebecca Booth, M.D., *The Venus Week: Discover the Powerful Secret of Your Cycle... At Any Age* (Cambridge: Da Capo Press, 2008). The Venus Week® is a registered trademark of Beauty Booth LLC. For more information on *The Venus Week* visit www.thevenusweek.com

2. Gloria Feldt, *The War on Choice: The Right-Wing Attack on Women's Rights and How to Fight Back* (New York: Bantam Books, 2004), 39.

3. Andrea Tone, *Controlling Reproduction, An American History,* The Worlds of Women Series (Lanham: Rowman & Littlefield, 1996).

4. Gloria Feldt, *The War on Choice*, 40 (see n. 2).

5. Bill Bryson, *At Home: A Short History of Private Life* (New York: Doubleday, 2010), 329-30.

6. "See Jane Do," KVMR, Nevada City Community Broadcast Group. Nevada City, CA: KVMR, October 5, 2011.

7. Leonard Shlain, *The Alphabet Versus the Goddess: The Conflict Between Word and Image* (New York: Penguin/Compass, 1998), 1.

8. Alanna Hartzog, "Democracy, Earth Rights and the Next Economy," originally presented at the *Twenty-First Annual E. F. Schumacher Lectures*, Amherst College, Amherst, Massachusetts, October 27, 2001, www.earthrights.net/docs/schumacher.html (February 2012).

9. University of Chicago. "Brain Waves Pattern Themselves After Rhythms Of Nature." *ScienceDaily*, 15 Feb. 2008, (June 2009).

10. CNRS. "Influence of the Menstrual Cycle on the Female Brain." *ScienceDaily*, 10 Feb. 2007, (April 2008).

11. Michael Gurian and Barbara Annis, *Leadership and the Sexes: Using Gender Science to Create Success in Business* (San Francisco: Jossey-Bass, 2008), 49.

12. Mintz, S. (2007). *Childbirth in Early America, Digital History*. Retrieved 4.28.2012 from www.digitalhistory.uh.edu/historyonline/childbirth.cfm

13. Janis Hunt Johnson, *Five Smooth Stones: Our Power to Heal Without Medicine Through the Science of Prayer* (Medford: CS Renewel, 2008).

14. T.S. Wiley, *The Wiley Protocol, Clinical Practice Guidelines*, pg. 20

15. Jian Lin, et al., "Plasticity of human menstrual blood stem cells derived from the endometrium," *Journal of Zehjiang University*, 2011, www.ncbi.nlm.nih.gov/pmc/articles/PMC3087093/ (26 April, 2012).

16. Michelle Roberts, "Concern over menstrual blood bank," *BBC News*, 2007, news.bbc.co.uk/2/hi/health/7086548.stm (26 April, 2012).

17. Neha Verma, "Menstrual blood banking: Scope and future," *MedIndia*, 2012, www.medindia.net/news/healthinfocus/Menstrual-Blood-Banking-Scope-and-Future-95616-1.htm (26 April, 2012).

18. Booth, *The Venus Week*® (see n. 1).

19. Wiley, *The Wiley Protocol*, 20 (see n. 14).

20. Booth, *The Venus Week*® (see n. 1).

21. "Understanding Ovulation," *American Pregnancy Association*, www.american-pregnancy.org/gettingpregnant/understandingovulation.html (September 2011)

22. "Understanding Ovulation," (see n. 21).

23. Booth, *The Venus Week*®, 19 (see n. 1).

24. "Understanding Ovulation" (see n. 21).

25. "How Pregnancy Happens," *Planned Parenthood*, www.plannedparenthood.org/health-topics/pregnancy/how-pregnancy-happens-4252.htm (September 2011).

26. "Understanding Miscarriage," *babycenter*, www.babycenter.com/0_understanding-miscarriage_252.bc (January 2011).

27. "How Long From Conception to Implantation?" *BabyHopes.com*, www.babyhopes.com/articles/conception-implantation.html (September 2010).

28. "Implantation," *Us Moms*, www.usmomssite.com/implantation (September 2010).

29. Booth, *The Venus Week*®, 103 (see n. 1).

30. Indiana University. "Women View Men's Faces Differently Depending On The Stage Of Their Menstrual Cycle." *ScienceDaily, 14 November 2007*. Web. 10 www.sciencedaily.com/releases/2007/11/071114182256.htm (22 April 2008).

31. Christiane Northrup, M.D., "Estrogen Dominance," www.drnorthrup.com/womenshealth/healthcenter/topic_details.php?topic_id=118 (January 2011).

32. "Infertility: Estrogen Dominance," *Shared Journey: Your Path to Fertility*, www.sharedjourney.com/infertility_estrogen.html (January 2011).

33. Tracey Roizman, D.C., "Ibuprofen Side Effects with Long Term Use," *Livestrong.com*, www.livestrong.com/article/102201-ibuprofen-side-effects-longterm-use/ (June 2011).

34. Ken Page, LCSW, "How Your Greatest Insecurities Reveal Your Deepest Gifts," *Psychology Today*, 2011, www.psychologytoday.com/blog/finding-love/201109/how-your-greatest-insecurities-reveal-your-deepest-gifts (March 2012).

Artist Credits

Mara Berendt Friedman Website: *www.newmoonvisions.com* Email: stream@newmoonvisions.com Phone: 800.701.6984 Page 27: Maluhia (Peace), 1994, 5"x7", hand-colored linoleum block print; 38: Olivia Cloud Walker, 2007, 16"x20", acrylic on canvas; 45: Tears of Joy, Water of Life, 2002, 17"x23", oil on canvas; 57: Dancing with the Sun, 1994, gouache and ink on paper; 107: She Goes With Grace, 1995, 18"x24", acrylic on canvas; 108: Fall, 2012, commissioned for *4 Seasons in 4 Weeks*, 14"x18", acrylic on canvas; 136: Winter, 2012, commissioned for *4 Seasons in 4 Weeks*, 14"x18", acrylic on canvas; 150: Open Heart, 1996, 8"x10", acrylic on canvas; 166: Spring, 2012, commissioned for *4 Seasons in 4 Weeks*, 14"x18", acrylic on canvas; 187: Homage to Modigliani, 1998, 8"x10", oil on canvas; 197: Strength of Heart, 2006, 16"x20", acrylic on canvas; 212: Summer, 2012, commissioned for *4 Seasons in 4 Weeks*, 14"x18", acrylic on canvas; 224: Sun Womb, 2000, 11⅞" x 11⅞", mixed media on panel; 242: Morning Prayer, 2005, 14"x18", acrylic on canvas; 244: Golden Opening, 2007, 12"x16", acrylic on canvas; 254: Prayer to the Sea, 1994, 8"x10", hand-colored linoleum block print.

Cathy McClelland Website: *www.CathyMcClelland.com* Email: cathy@cathymc-clelland.com Page 89: Atlantis Temple-Malta, 2010, 11"x15", acrylic on watercolor board; 154: Wisteria Nights, 2002, 3'x6', acrylic on canvas; 157: The Star, 2006, 11"x17", acrylic on watercolor board; 159: June Moon, 1996, 4'x5', acrylic on canvas; 165: Wolf Medicine, 2011, 9"x9", acrylic on canvas; 183: Destiny of Two Stars, 2002, 3.5'x5.5', acrylic on canvas; 199: Justice, 2006, 11"x17", acrylic on watercolor board; 237: Finding Peace, 2007, 16"x20", acrylic on canvas; 253: Golden Lion, 2011, 9"x9", acrylic on canvas; 292: A Place for Sacred Dreams and Wishes, 2004, 11"x13", acrylic on watercolor board.

Krista Lynn Brown Website: *www.devaluna.com* Email: devaluna@sbcglobal.net Page 87: Time Was, 14"x18", acrylic; 120: Sleeping Siren, 16"x20", acrylic; 124: Sigh, 8"x10", acrylic; 129: Heart Offering, 16"x20", acrylic; 193: Blue, 8"x8", acrylic; 211: The Beloveds, 18"x24", acrylic; 299: One With the Sweetness, 24"x30", acrylic; 303: Black Venus, 24"x36", acrylic.

Jen Otey/Moonbow Artworks Website: *www.Moonbowartworks.com* Email: moonbowartworks@yahoo.com Page 59: We of the Moon, 2006, 8"x12", acrylic; 62: Gaia Tree, 2003, 10"x16", acrylic; 229: Burn (adjusted), 2008, 10"x24", acrylic.

Betty LaDuke Website: *www.bettyladuke.com* Email: bladuke@jeffnet.org Page 69: Jamaica Tomorrow, 1986, 60"x54", acrylic; 93: Mandala for Peace, 2009, 48"x40", router-shaped plywood panel; 280: Uganda, Green Bananas, 2005, 54"x50", acrylic.

Denise Kester Website: *www.drawingonthedream.com* Email: denisekester@drawingonthedream.com Page 32: Mother Natura, 2010, 10"x13" (16"x20" framed), monoprint.

Cat Stone (Hawkins) Websites: *www.naturalshaman.blogspot.com* *www.meetmypmdd.blogspot.com www.chaoticat.com* Page 66: Goddess Mandala, 2006, 20cmx20cm, colored pencil and fine liners.

Pegi Smith Website: *www.pegismith.com* Email: Pegi@PegiSmith.com Page 28: In My Cocoon, 24"x24", acrylic on wrapped canvas; 34: Years of Tears Beyond the Fears, 24"x30", acrylic on wrapped canvas; 77: Lovers, 12"x46", acrylic and mixed media.

Andrew Bonsall, Medical Illustrator/Teacher Email: abonsall@hbuhsd.edu Charts (Adobe Illustrator) on pages 95, 114, 143, 173, 220, 276, 277.

Lorraine Leslie Website: *Lorraineleslie.blogspot.com* Email: Shivashakti23@msn.com Page 46: Winter Solstice, 2010, 18"x24", acrylic on canvas.

Clio Wondrausch Website: *www.wildhearth.co.uk* Email: clio@wildhearth.co.uk Page 61: Beloved Water 2, 2005, 1mx80cm, found and naturally prepared earth pigments on carpet underlay; 72: Offering of Love, 2004, 1mx80cm, found and naturally prepared earth pigments on carpet underlay; 75: Blood Keeper, 2006, 55cmx102cm, found and naturally prepared earth pigments on hand-spun cloth; 123: Silent Echoes, 2003, 100cmx82cm, found and naturally prepared earth pigments on carpet underlay; 153: Warm at the Hearth, 2000, 109cmx70cm, found and naturally prepared earth pigments on old French linen sheet.

Louise Abel Curtis Page 90: 4s4w Moon Mandala, 2012, commissioned for *4 Seasons in 4 Weeks,* 15"x15", Prismacolor Pencil; p. 276: Correspondence and ceremonial charts development.

Victoria Christian Website: *www.victoriachristian.com* Email: electrart@ hotmail.com Page 81: Anna's Surprise, 2000, 18"x24", pastel on paper.

Tzila "Z" Duenzl Email: mtwoman@gmail.com Page 48: Gourd Petal, photograph; 49: Sunflower Geometry, photograph; 50: Water Lily, photograph.

Inger Jorgensen Website: *www.ingerjorgensen.com* Page 279: Illuminate the Inside, 2007, 36"x40", oil on canvas.

Damian Fulton Email: dxfulton@gmail.com Page 231: Marie, 1985, 2007, 36"x48", oil.

Cecile Miranda *cecilemirandafineart.com* Page 233: Fire Walker, 2012, commissioned for *4 Seasons in 4 Weeks*, 40" x 30" acrylic on canvas.

Special thanks: Photoshop and/or Scanning: Harmonic Design, Talent, OR, Sterling Editions, Springfield, OR, Robert Jaffe, Medford, OR, Pat Moore, Talent, OR, Nils Vidstrand Studios, Los Angeles, CA.

Order now at 4seasons4weeks.com:

◆ *4 Seasons in 4 Weeks: Awakening the Power, Wisdom, and Beauty of Every Woman's Nature* ◆

◆ 4s4w Two-month Daily Tracker and Journal ◆

◆ **The 4s4w Tracker Phone App** ◆

◆ 4s4w Refrigerator Magnets ◆

◆ **The 4s4w ManGuide and other companion guides** ◆

◆ 4s4w Gift Items ◆

Download a FREE full–size Monthly Tracker and instructions!

✦ Choose between cycling and non-cycling charts

✦ Become attentive to the various cycles within your monthly rhythm

THE 4S4W MONTHLY TRACKER WILL HELP YOU ANSWER THESE QUESTIONS AND MANY MORE:

1. What day am I on in my cycle? What significant role does this play in my life?

2. When is my energy consistently high (or low) in any given month?

3. When do I feel the most loving and giving?

4. Is there a particular time of the month when I am more susceptible to illness?

5. How do I identify my "hot spots?" How do they serve me?

6. When are the best times to be with my partner? When are the best times to go inward?

7. When is my most creative time?

8. When must I be disciplined about rest?

9. How can I predict my changing mental outlook?

10. What is the pattern of my sex drive?